Paul Des Marais

Department of Music
University of California, Los Angeles

HARMONY:
A Workbook in Fundamentals

 W · W · NORTON & COMPANY · INC · *New York*

MT
50
.D4 x

Music prepared by Irwin Rabinowitz

PREFACE

This workbook is intended to fulfill two functions: the first is a selective re-interpretation of those aspects of harmony that in the author's experience often need to be emphasized and repeated; the second lies in the body of written and keyboard exercises, which, it is hoped, will challenge the student's ingenuity and sharpen his awareness.

The justification for this workbook lies in the author's teaching experience in harmony. Seldom have his classes been of a uniform scholastic level. The experienced student will quickly grasp the fundamentals of this field and will act on them in a capable manner; the student with relatively little musical experience will need more time and more patience. Perhaps both of them, after having understood and worked out the exercises in this workbook, will handle more demanding material with fluency.

The workbook is intended as a corollary to Walter Piston's *Harmony* (Third Edition), a text that the author has used with gratifying results for a good number of years. Each chapter of the workbook notes at the beginning its required reading in the Piston text and can be most successfully understood and worked out with that text.

Although the two books move in a parallel manner, Piston's chronology has been violated in the workbook in two instances. Chapter Fifteen in the workbook, the chapter on sequence, anticipates the required reading from Piston's text. The author feels that the student can benefit by being involved in keyboard sequences before he studies the diminished seventh chord and the more advanced forms of dominant harmony. If the teacher prefers to follow the chronology of Piston's text, the keyboard exercises in sequence can be postponed until the appropriate time.

The second violation in chronology involves the diminished seventh chord. In Chapter Sixteen of the workbook it is treated in both its dominant and nondominant capacities. The author strongly feels that such a summation of this chord is necessary at some point in the study of harmony, particularly since this chord, in nineteenth-century music, often shifts from a dominant to a nondominant interpretation.

The music suggested for study and analysis is all available in accessible and inexpensive editions. Although great care has been exercised in the selection of the music to be studied, from the standpoint of relevance, some excerpts and complete compositions will contain chords and procedures in advance of the student's knowledge.

The author wishes to express his profound gratitude to Professor William Mitchell for his patient reading of the manuscript and for his penetrating criticisms and suggestions.

Paul Des Marais
Los Angeles   1962.

CONTENTS

I / SCALES AND INTERVALS

Required reading: Piston, Chapter 1.

SCALES

Common-practice melody and harmony are based upon three different scales: the major scale, the minor scale with its melodic and harmonic forms, and the chromatic scale. Attention in this chapter will be focused upon only the major and the melodic minor scales.

It will be observed that while the major scale remains the same in its ascending and descending form, the melodic minor scale undergoes changes in respect to its sixth and seventh degrees. Although the use of the minor mode in the music of the Baroque, Classical, and Romantic periods is indeed a complex and subtle matter, some preliminary statements may be made at this point:

(1) the sixth and seventh degrees, when used in their ascending form, tend to move upward;

(2) the sixth and seventh degrees, when used in their descending form, tend to move downward;

(3) the melodic interval of the augmented second created by the descending form of the sixth degree and the ascending form of the seventh degree is normally avoided in melodic construction.

The following fragments should help to clarify these statements:

CLASSIFICATION OF INTERVALS

The following is a list of all the practical intervals to be found in common-practice harmony and melody. One can, of course, find intervals other than those listed; they must be looked for in music of a highly chromatic nature, however, and cannot be considered as other than exceptional.

Intervals may change their size by means of chromatic alteration. As an example, the perfect fifth formed by the notes C and G becomes an augmented fifth if the G is altered to become G-sharp. To the beginning student of harmony, the nomenclature of these 'changed' intervals might seem inexcusably difficult. The following statements, however, should clarify the process:

(1) a perfect interval may expand to become augmented and contract to become diminished;

(2) a major interval may expand to become augmented and contract to become minor;

(3) a minor interval may expand to become major and contract to become diminished.

INTERVAL INVERSION

Inversion, in reference to harmonic intervals, means simply an exchange: if the top and bottom notes reverse their position, the interval is considered inverted.

The result of interval inversion from the standpoint of classification can be summarized by the following pair of statements:

(1) perfect intervals remain perfect; major intervals become minor, and minor intervals become major; diminished intervals become augmented, and augmented intervals become diminished;

(2) the numerical sum of any given interval and its inversion is 9.

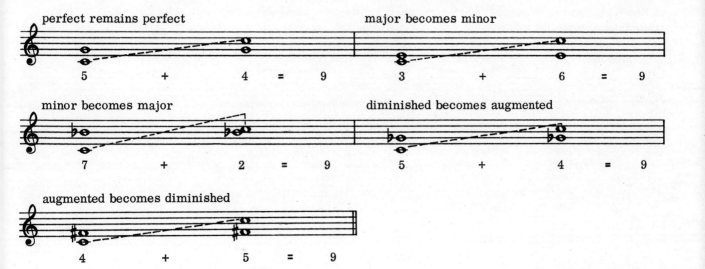

perfect remains perfect

5   +   4   =   9

major becomes minor

3   +   6   =   9

minor becomes major

7   +   2   =   9

diminished becomes augmented

5   +   4   =   9

augmented becomes diminished

4   +   5   =   9

EXERCISES

I. SCALES

1. The student of harmony should be able to play and to write the major and minor
scales in all keys, and a keyboard familiarity with them is the purpose of these exercises.
The harmonic form of the minor scale is not intended to be used in these exercises: such an
emphasis on the augmented second interval present in the harmonic form might mislead the
student when he moves on to the writing of exercises in the minor mode.

Pattern A

Pattern B

Pattern C

Pattern D

Play scale pattern A in the following keys: G major, D major, E minor, and B minor.

Play scale pattern B in the following keys: A-flat major, E-flat major, F minor, and C minor.

Play scale pattern C in the following keys: B-flat major, D-flat major, E-flat minor, and B-flat minor.

2. The following excerpts are written in the melodic minor scale. Working on the assumption that the sixth and seventh degrees, when used in their ascending form, tend to move upward, and that the same degrees, when used in their descending form, tend to move downward, make those chromatic alterations which are appropriate.

A Dowland—*Can She Excuse My Wrongs*?

B Dowland—*Flow, My Tears*.

C Buxtehude—*Wo soll ich fliehen hin*.

D Dowland—*If My Complaints Could Passions Move.*

E Schubert—*Ständchen.*

II. CLASSIFICATION OF INTERVALS

Note: the change of an interval is customarily thought of as involving a change in the upper note. Such a view is the result of attempts to simplify the problems of interval measurement. The change of an interval may just as likely involve a change in the lower note, however, and the student of harmony must be able to visualize, or write, any given interval from any given upper or lower note. The following exercises have this knowledge as their aim.

(a) with C as the lower note, play or write the following intervals: perfect unison, perfect fifth, major third, major sixth, perfect fourth, major second, major seventh, and perfect octave.

(b) repeat this procedure with the following lower notes: G and D.

(c) with E-flat as the upper note, play or write the following intervals: perfect fourth, minor sixth, minor third, perfect fifth, minor seventh, minor second, and perfect octave.

(d) repeat this procedure with the following upper notes: B-flat and F.

(e) with D-flat as the lower note, play or write the following intervals: minor sixth, perfect fifth, major seventh, perfect octave, perfect fourth, minor third, major second, and perfect unison.

(f) repeat this procedure with the following lower notes: A-flat and E-flat.

(g) with F as the upper note, play or write the following intervals: major third, perfect fourth, minor second, perfect unison, minor seventh, perfect fifth, major sixth, and perfect octave.

(h) repeat this procedure with the following upper notes: C and G.

(i) with C as the lower note, play or write the following intervals: augmented second, augmented fifth, augmented fourth, augmented sixth, diminished fifth, and diminished seventh.

(j) with D as the upper note, play or write the following intervals: augmented sixth, augmented second, augmented fourth, diminished fifth, diminished seventh, and augmented fifth.

(k) with E as the lower note, play or write the following intervals: augmented second, diminished fifth, augmented fourth, augmented sixth, augmented fifth, and diminished seventh.

(l) with F as the upper note, play or write the following intervals: diminished seventh, diminished fifth, augmented sixth, augmented fourth, augmented fifth, and augmented second.

(m) with G as the lower note, play or write the following intervals: augmented fifth, diminished seventh, diminished fifth, augmented fourth, augmented second, and augmented sixth.

(n) with A as the upper note, play or write the following intervals: diminished seventh, augmented fifth, augmented sixth, augmented fourth, diminished fifth, and augmented second.

III. INTERVAL "PLAY"

The following exercises are intended for the keyboard, but may be written out if they exceed the pianistic abilities of the student. As written exercises, they should, of course, cover only one octave in range. As keyboard exercises, the student should be aware, at all times, of the correct notation of the intervals which he is playing.

(a) Play the chromatic scale ascending and descending two octaves, beginning on middle C, and repeat beneath it the following series of intervals: octave, perfect fourth, and minor third;

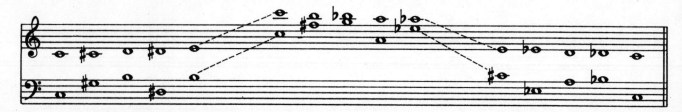

Repeat the procedure starting on D and G above middle C;

(b) Play the chromatic scale ascending and descending two octaves, beginning an octave below middle C, and repeat above it the following series of intervals: octave, perfect fourth, and minor third;

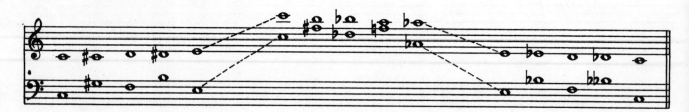

Repeat the procedure starting on F and on B-flat below middle C;

(c) Play the chromatic scale ascending and descending two octaves, beginning on middle C, and repeat beneath it the following series of intervals: octave, perfect fourth, major sixth, and major third;

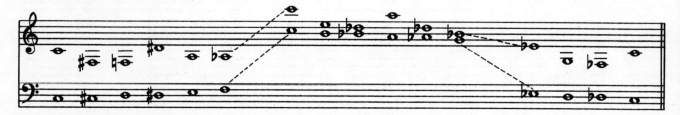

Repeat the procedure starting on D and G above middle C;

(d) Play the chromatic scale ascending and descending two octaves, beginning an octave

10

below middle C, and repeat above it the following series of intervals: octave, perfect fourth, major sixth, and major third;

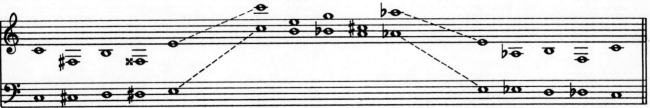

Repeat the procedure starting on F and B-flat below middle C.

II / TRIADS

Required reading: Piston, Chapter 2.

The triad, a chord made up of a ladder of thirds, has three positions, calculated not from the top down but from the bottom up: (1) the root position in which the root of the triad, its bottom note, is in the bass; (2) the first inversion in which the third of the triad, its middle note, is in the bass; and (3) the second inversion in which the fifth of the triad, its top note, is in the bass.

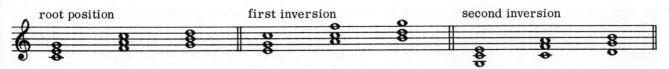

Triads are built upon every degree of the major and minor scales and consist of four different kinds: major, minor, augmented, and diminished. The major and minor triads derive their classification from the interval formed by their bottom and middle notes; the diminished and augmented triads derive their classification from the interval formed by their bottom and top notes. Of the four kinds of triads, the major and minor are consonant, the augmented and diminished are dissonant. This is another way of saying that major and minor triads are stable while augmented and diminished triads are unstable and demand a resolution of the tension which they create. Since this chapter is concerned with types of triads rather than with how they move, the problem of resolving dissonant triads will be reserved for Chapter 3. The immediate problem is to recognize clearly and easily the difference, in sound and notation, between the four different kinds.

In determining the different kinds of triad to be found in a minor key, the harmonic form of the scale is used. The reasons for this choice are several; the simple explanation would seem to be the tendency, in a minor key, to keep the subdominant a minor triad and the dominant a major triad. A progression using the three most important triads of the scale, I, IV, and V, and observing this tendency, "creates" the harmonic form of the minor scale.

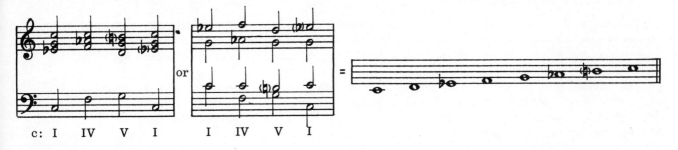

Looking at the progressions in the previous example from the standpoint of the melodic tendencies described in Chapter One, it will be observed that the sixth degree, in its descending form, does indeed move downward, that the seventh degree, in its ascending form, does indeed move upward, and that the melodic interval of the augmented second is present in no individual part, or voice.

13

There is no conflict between the melodic and harmonic approaches to the minor scale. Under certain conditions, one approach will take precedence over the other, for no musical situation is without some problem or complication. The student is best served at the present time not by exceptions to the rule but by the following statements:

(1) the sixth and seventh degrees, in their ascending form, tend to move upward, and in their descending form tend to move downward;

(2) the melodic interval of the augmented second is normally avoided in all individual parts, or voices;

(3) the subdominant triad is normally minor, and the dominant triad is almost always major.

DOUBLING

Since the triad is a three-note chord and harmony exercises are traditionally written for four voices, soprano, alto, tenor and bass, it is obvious that one of the chord tones will have to be doubled. In root-position harmony, the root of the triad is the tone most frequently doubled. The fifth of the triad may also be doubled. The third of the triad is least frequently doubled, and only as a last possibility.

root doubled   fifth doubled   third doubled

Although all three notes of the triad are normally present in four-part writing, a particular melodic problem may make it advisable to omit one of the chord tones. The fifth of the triad is then omitted, and the root is tripled.

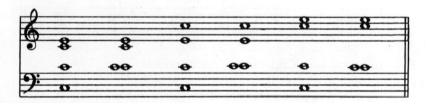

CLOSE AND OPEN POSITION

A triad may be written in either close or open position. In close position the three upper voices are placed upon adjacent chord tones; in open position a "space" or unused chord tone is present between the soprano and the alto, between the alto and the tenor, or between both.

The following is a series of possible scorings in both close and open position of the complete triad in root position. It is, incidentally, limited to those scorings in which the root of the triad is doubled. It should be studied closely in reference to the statements which follow, for they are meant to serve as an effective guide to scoring.

(1) In close position the soprano, the alto, and the tenor are written in the upper staff, the bass in the lower staff;

(2) in open position the soprano and the alto are written in the upper staff, the tenor and the bass in the lower staff;

(3) in open position the distance between either the soprano and the alto or between the alto and the tenor seldom exceeds the range of an octave;

(4) in both close and open position, the outer parts seldom exceed the range of two octaves and a fifth.

EXERCISES

1. The following pattern consists of a succession of triads (major, augmented, diminished, and minor) built from a fixed bottom note:

Play this pattern on all twelve chromatic degrees, starting on C and ending on C an octave higher. The student should be prepared to spell any triad just played if the teacher interrupts his performance to ask its spelling.

2. The following pattern consists of the same succession of triads in a more elaborate texture:

Play this pattern through a circle of fifths, beginning and ending with C as the bottom note.

3. Answer the following questions in reference to the major and harmonic minor scales only.

(a)   Triad *1* is I in what major key?
                IV in what major key?
                V in what major or minor key?
                VI in what minor key?

(b)   Triad *2* is III in what minor key?

(c)   Triad *3* is II in what minor key?
                VII in what major key?

(d)   Triad *4* is I in what minor key?
                II in what major key?
                III in what major key?
                IV in what minor key?
                VI in what major key?

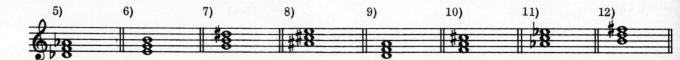

(e) In what major and minor keys and upon what scale degrees are each of the preceding triads to be found?

4. The following pattern consists of an open-position scoring of a triad in root position, first inversion, second inversion, and again root position:

The pattern may be played in the following manner:

(a) as a *major* triad, moving up chromatically from C to C an octave higher;

(b) as a *minor* triad, moving up chromatically from C to C an octave higher;

(c) as a *major* triad, moving through a circle of fifths, beginning and ending with C:

(d) as a *minor* triad, moving through a circle of fifths, beginning and ending with C.

5. The following exercises are to be played, not written; the following model question should illustrate the procedure.

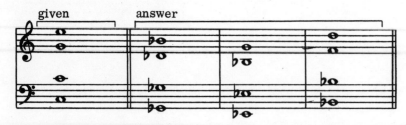

Using the given scoring at all times, play three different major triads that contain the note B-flat:

scoring 1   scoring 2

Using *Scoring 1* of the triad at all times, complete the following:

(a) play three different major triads which contain the note F;

(b) play three different minor triads which contain the note B;

(c) play three different major triads which contain the note G-sharp;

(d) play three different minor triads which contain the note D.

Using *Scoring 2* of the triad at all times, complete the following:

(e) play three different major triads which contain the note F-sharp;

(f) play three different minor triads which contain the note C;

(g) play three different major triads which contain the note A;

(h) play three different minor triads which contain the note E-flat.

6.   Triads in root position and with the root doubled are to be used in the following exercises.

(a) write three different major triads in open position with C in the soprano;

(b) write three different minor triads in close position with E-flat in the alto;

(c) write three different major triads in close position with F-sharp in the tenor;

(d) write three different minor triads in open position with A in the soprano;

(e) write three different major triads in close position with E in the alto;

(f) write three different minor triads in open position with G in the tenor;

(g) write three different major triads in open position with B-flat in the soprano;

(h) write three different minor triads in close position with C-sharp in the alto.

III / HARMONIC PROGRESSION

Required reading: Piston, Chapter 3.

ROOT MOVEMENT

Tonality is posited on the belief that certain scale degrees, serving as roots of triads, are more important than others. In the mind of a composer of the common-practice period, the tonic, or first degree, was considered the most important of all, and it was, in his composition, both the point of departure and the point of return. Next in importance was the dominant, or fifth degree; last, but still important, was the subdominant, or fourth degree.

These three degrees, serving as roots of triads, were the pillars in the architecture of the phrase and of the entire composition.

C: I   V   I   IV   I

It will be seen that the interval formed by the tonic and dominant degrees and by the tonic and subdominant degrees is that of a fifth. Indeed, root movement of a fifth, operating on all degrees of the scale, may be considered the basic ingredient of common-practice harmony. The following example is only one of the many that can be found to demonstrate the importance and prominence of this particular kind of root movement.

Mozart—*Sonata in A minor, K. 310*

There are, in addition to root movement of a fifth, two other kinds: (1) root movement of a third, and (2) stepwise root movement, and the root, in all three cases, may either ascend or descend. The student is referred to his required reading for an explanation of the subtle differences between the two possibilities.

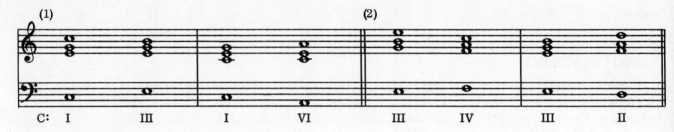

Root movements of a fourth, a sixth, and a seventh are not additional kinds but, rather, variants of the root movements already described from the standpoint of the motion of the bass. As an example, the progression V-I is based on root movement of a descending fifth regardless of whether the bass moves down a fifth or up a fourth.

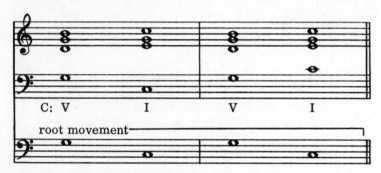

RESOLUTION OF DISSONANT TRIADS

The supertonic triad in a minor key is a diminished triad and, in contrast to the leading-tone triad, is used in root position. The mediant triad in a minor key is an augmented triad and is also used in root position. How are the dissonant intervals contained in each of these chords resolved?

It will be observed that the top note of the diminished fifth contained in II resolves downward and that the top note of the augmented fifth contained in III resolves upward. The root movement of both progressions is that of a descending fifth: II-V, and III-VI.

VOICE LEADING

Harmony exercises are traditionally written for four voices: soprano, alto, tenor, and bass. This specification is a good one for it forces the student to think about harmony as a web of voices rather than as a succession of "blocks." Harmony *is* counterpoint to a great degree.

The inner voices of a harmony exercise will always be somewhat limited in their motion and their interest; attention will be focused mainly on the outer voices.

The problem of harmonic progression is not only the problem of good root movement but also of good voice leading. The manner in which voices should move, by themselves and in relation to each other, should be clarified by the following statements.

(1) All voices tend to move more by step than by skip. After a skip of a fourth or of a larger interval, the voice tends to move in the opposite direction;

C: I   VI   V   I   I   IV   V   I   I   V   III VI   II   V   I

(2) the soprano and bass tend to move more in contrary and oblique than in similar motion;

Bach—*Die goldene Sonne, voll Freud' und Wonne*

(3) the soprano almost always moves from the leading tone by step, normally up to the tonic and on occasion down to the submediant;

(4) no two voices should move in parallel unisons, octaves, or fifths;

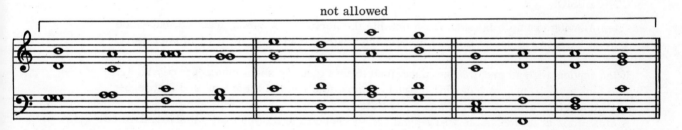

(5) no voice should skip past the previous note of the voice above or below it;

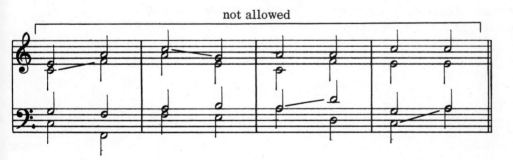

(6) if the soprano and bass move in similar motion either up or down to a fifth or an octave, one of the voices should move by step. Furthermore, if the soprano and bass move in similar motion up to an octave, the soprano should move by half step;

23

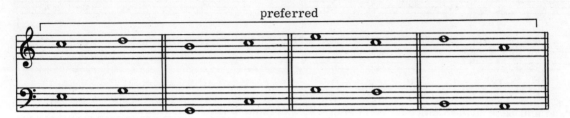

avoided

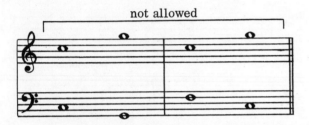

preferred

(7) the soprano and bass should not move, even in contrary motion, from one fifth to another or from one octave to another.

not allowed

It should be obvious that similar motion, when involved with perfect intervals, is one of the fundamental problems of voice leading.

CONCLUSION

The following example is taken from outside the period of common practice, but since the study of harmony is one of musical procedures rather than of style, its inclusion is relevant.

If the tendencies and prohibitions described in this chapter seem unnecessarily restrictive, the fact must be acknowledged that art is impossible without technique and that technique is impossible without control and restraint.

A close look at this example will reveal the following: the motion of the individual voice is strongly conjunct; the outer voices move more in oblique and contrary than in similar motion; and, most important of all, the succession of chords is enlivened by the way in which the voices move.

The felicitous combination of chord and line is indeed the goal of written work in harmony, and, like any artistic goal, it can be achieved only with restrictions and not without them.

Es ist ein Ros entsprungen

1. Es ist ein Ros ent-sprun-gen/ aus ei-ner Wur — zel zart/ als uns die
Al -ten sun - gen/ aus Jes- se kam die Art/ und hat ein Blüm-lein bracht/
mit - ten im kal-ten Win - ter/ wohl zu der hal - ben Nacht.

2. Das Röslein das ich meine/
Davon Esaias sagt/
Hat uns gebracht alleine/
Marie die reine Magd/
Aus Gottes ewgem Rat/
Hat sie ein Kind geboren/
Wohl zu der halben Nacht.

EXERCISES

1. Write or play two different arrangements in close position of each of the following harmonic progressions:

V–I in C major	I–VI in E major
V–VI in A minor	IV–V in D major
IV–I in G minor	VI–IV in B minor.

2. Write or play two different arrangements in open position of each of the following harmonic progressions:

V–I in B major	I–VI in G major
V–VI in A minor	IV–V in A major
IV–I in E minor	VI–IV in C minor.

3. Write or play three different progressions, all beginning with the same given chord. The spacing and position (close or open) of the given chord must remain unchanged for all three progressions. Furthermore, the given chord and the chords which are chosen to follow it should, whenever possible, be in the same position.

Note: only two different progressions are required for those chords marked by an asterisk (*).

4. Supply the missing notes in each of the following phrases, and give careful consideration to the voice leading and doubling involved. All of the chords are root-position triads. Do not hesitate to change from one position to the other if the voice leading benefits from it.

D major

30

D minor

A minor

A major

5. Play or write two different harmonizations in close position for each of the following melodic excerpts:

C major · B minor · A major

G minor · F major · E minor

Note: the harmonizations are intended to be somewhat, not completely, different. The progressions I-IV-V-I and VI-IV-V-I are different even though they have several chords in common.

6. Play or write two different arrangements in open position of the following succession of chords:

C minor: I–IV–V–VI–IV–I.

IV / TONALITY AND MODALITY

Required reading: Piston, Chapter 4.

Melody and harmony in the common-practice period are based upon two modes, the major and the minor, and these two modes are, in a sense, the distillation of a variety of modes, or scales, that were used in the medieval and renaissance periods.

The two modes, major and minor, differ only in regard to the mediant and submediant degrees and these degrees, affected by the shift from major to minor, are termed modal degrees. The important degrees of the scale are the tonic, dominant, and subdominant. They are termed tonal degrees, and considered from the standpoint of harmony they do indeed articulate the tonality, whether it be major or minor. The supertonic degree, with its close harmonic relation to the subdominant, is also considered a tonal degree. The leading-tone degree, which seldom serves as the root of a triad but is almost always incorporated into some form of the dominant chord, is not involved in this distinction.

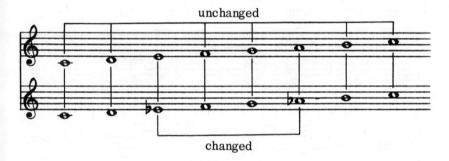

TONAL AND MODAL EMPHASIS

A melody in a major key can be harmonized in two distinctly different ways: (1) with an emphasis on tonal-degree triads, and (2) with an emphasis on modal-degree triads.

The first harmonization results in a strong tonal emphasis, and there is no question as to either key or mode. The second harmonization, on the other hand, creates a definite ambiguity: it can be interpreted in either the major key or in its relative minor. To be even more precise, the second harmonization refers to the Aeolian mode with its whole-step distance between leading-tone and tonic degrees.

modal emphasis

F: I   VI   III   VI   II   V   III   VI   II   III   etc.

For this reason the student of harmony must pay careful attention to the relative emphasis on tonal-, as opposed to modal-degree triads. Unless a modal emphasis is intended, the tonic, dominant, and subdominant triads must figure prominently.

INTERCHANGEABILITY OF THE MODES

In the nineteenth century the shift from one mode to the other played an increasingly important role in the development and expansion of the harmonic vocabulary. At the beginning, the two triads involved were the supertonic and the subdominant. A composition in a major key would often use these triads as they were constituted in a minor key. This shift of mode gradually began to involve triads on other degrees of the scale as well, and the result was a music that was neither strictly major nor minor, but a combination of both.

C: I   IV   V   VI   III   VI   II   V   I

In the preceding example a major key borrows from its minor equivalent, and it is important to understand the fact that this is by far more common than the reverse procedure. Furthermore, although II, III, IV, and VI are shifted in mode, V and, of course, I, remain unchanged. Melodic pressures may make the dominant triad minor, but it functions most effectively when it is major. And at this stage the student should be well aware of the profound importance of the dominant chord in the establishment of tonality.

EXERCISES

1. The following progression involves a change of mode for the subdominant triad:

C: I   IV   V   I

Play or write this progression in the following major keys: C, E-flat, F-sharp, A, D, F, A-flat, B, C-sharp, E, G, and B-flat.

2. The following progression may be played or written in three different ways:

(1) as written, in the major mode;

(2) in the minor mode;

(3) in the major mode with the subdominant triad shifted to the minor mode.

Play or write the preceding progression in the following major keys: C, E-flat, and A.

Play or write the preceding progression in the following minor keys: F, B, and E.

Play or write the preceding progression in the following major keys with the subdominant triad shifted to the minor mode: C-sharp, F, and A-flat.

*Since this is a keyboard exercise the presence of a triad in first inversion should create no difficulties.

3. Given the following harmonic skeleton, make a four-part setting in open position in the key of E major:

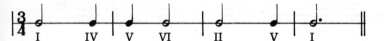

Play or write this same setting in the key of F-sharp minor.

4. Given the following harmonic skeleton, make a four-part setting in open position in the key of A-flat major:

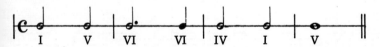

Play or write this same setting in the key of B-flat minor.

5. Make two different four-part settings in open position of the following melody. The first setting should emphasize tonal-degree triads and the second setting should emphasize modal-degree triads.

C major

6. Make two different four-part settings in close position of each of the following melodic fragments. The first setting should be completely diatonic and the second setting should involve a shift of mode for the subdominant and submediant triads whenever they are used. Each of the melodic fragments is in a different major key.

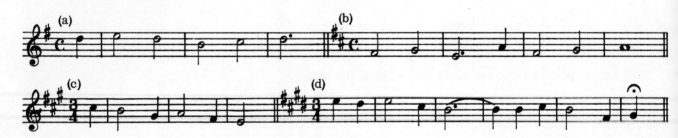

V / CHORDS OF THE SIXTH

Required reading: Piston, Chapter 5.

    A close study of the harmonic formulae encountered in the required reading for this chapter is particularly important, for it reveals the following tendencies in regard to chord motion:

    (1) the *bass* of a chord of the sixth is more likely to move on by step or by skip than to remain on the same note. When the bass does remain on the same note, the harmonic effect is static;

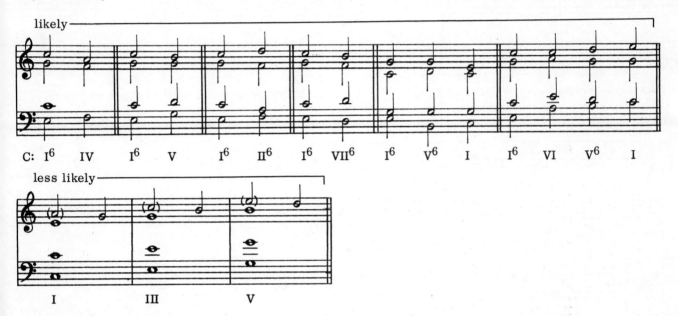

    (2) the *root* of a chord of the sixth is more likely to move on by skip of a fifth or by step rather than by skip of a third. The root movement of the progressions in the above example should illustrate this tendency.

DOUBLING

    The question of doubling with a chord of the sixth is answered by referring to the degrees of the scale involved rather than to the chord itself. Those degrees that strengthen the tonality are doubled in preference to those degrees that weaken it. The tonic, supertonic, subdominant, and dominant degrees of the scale are doubled in preference to the mediant and submediant degrees. The leading-tone degree, with its strong tendency to move up to the tonic, is seldom doubled.

    The student must always keep in mind the fact that the motion of the voices takes precedence over doubling, that there are situations where the doubling of a modal degree is advisable. In the light of this fact, the different kinds of doubling listed below are given the classification "preferred" and "avoided" rather than "right" and "wrong."

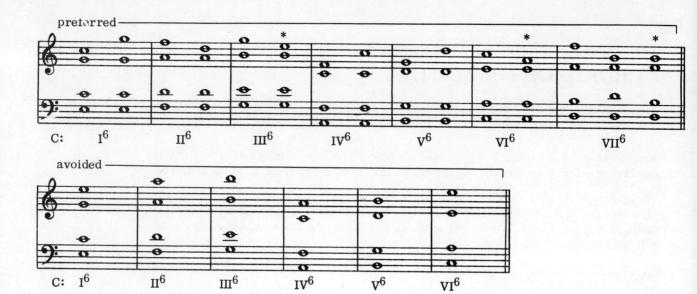

The chords marked with an asterisk (*) involve doubling that is normally avoided. These particular scorings are used, however, when they progress in the manner indicated by the following example and are often found in sequential passages.

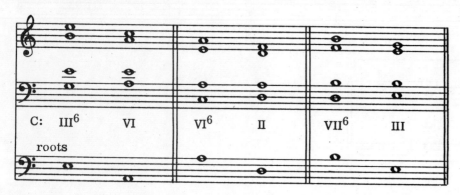

44

EXERCISES

1. Play or write a four-part setting in close position of the following progressions:

   I-VII^6-I^6-IV in C major (with C as the first note in the soprano)

   VI-II^6-V-I^6 in E major (with E as the first note in the soprano)

   IV^6-V-I^6 in A-flat major (with D-flat as the first note in the soprano)

   I-VII^6-I^6-IV in D minor (with F as the first note in the soprano)

   VI-II^6-V-I^6 in F-sharp minor (with A as the first note in the soprano)

   IV^6-V-I^6 in B-flat minor (with B-flat as the first note in the soprano).

2. Play or write a four-part setting in open position of the following progressions:

   I-IV^6-II^6-V-I in E major (with E as the first note in the soprano)

   I-V-VI-IV^6-V-I in A-flat major (with C as the first note in the soprano)

   II-I^6-II^6-V-I in C major (with F as the first note in the soprano)

   I-IV^6-II^6-V-I in F-sharp minor (with C-sharp as the first note in the soprano)

   I-V-VI-IV^6-V-I in B-flat minor (with F as the first note in the soprano)

   II-I^6-II^6-V-I in D minor (with G as the first note in the soprano).

3. Play or write a four-part setting in close position of the following progressions in different major keys:

I^6-IV-V-I

I-VII^6-I^6-IV-I

I^6-II^6-III^6-VI

I^6-V-VI-V-I

4. Play or write a four-part setting in open position of the following progressions in different major keys:

> III^6-VI-II^6-I
>
> III^6-VI-V^6-I
>
> III^6-VI-IV-I

5. Write a four-part setting in open position of each of the following melodies and use chords of the sixth only where indicated.

Note: the melodic form of the minor scale should be used for the harmonization of the melody in A minor.

E minor   VI   II^6

B♭ major   IV^6 V^6 II^6

G minor   III^6 II^6 VI

A major   V^6 IV   IV^6 II^6 I^6

C minor   IV^6 II^6 I^6 V^6 IV^6 VI^6 IV^6 (V)

E minor   IV⁶   IV⁶   IV⁶   I⁶

C major   VII⁶ I⁶   II⁶   III⁶ IV⁶ V⁶   V⁶ IV⁶ III⁶ II⁶   II⁶

A minor   V⁶ IV⁶ III⁶ II⁶   IV⁶ V⁶   IV⁶ I⁶ _____ II⁶ III⁶ IV⁶ V⁶   IV⁶ V⁶   II⁶

This passing-tone is supported by the harmony that precedes it.

6. Make two different four-part settings in open position of the following melody. The first setting should use root-position triads only, and the second may use both root-position triads and chords of the sixth.

G major

7. STUDY AND ANALYSIS

Although complete and detailed harmonic analysis is impossible at this stage, the student could still benefit greatly from playing and listening to a selected number of Bach chorales. During this activity, his attention should be centered upon chords of the sixth and upon the manner in which they effect a smooth and fluid bass line. He may also become aware of the fact that a chord of the sixth has very little feeling of finality, that it strongly implies further motion.

The following chorales are suggested for study. Other chorales may, of course, be used: they should be fairly simple and diatonic, however, so that the student does not have to "fight" his way through an elaborate texture to find the chords of the sixth. These chorales are taken from *371 Harmonized Chorales by Johann Sebastian Bach*, Albert Riemenschneider, editor, New York, G. Schirmer, Inc., 1941.

26. *O Ewigkeit, du Donnerwort*

93. *Wach' auf, mein Herz*

42. *Du Friedensfürst, Herr Jesu Christ*

74. *O Haupt voll Blut und Wunden*

102. *Ermuntre dich, mein schwacher Geist*

217. *Ach Gott, wie manches Herzeleid*

VI / THE HARMONIC STRUCTURE OF THE PHRASE

Required reading: Piston, Chapter 6.

   The music of the common-practice period breathes, as we breathe, in a regular and
symmetrical manner. Almost any given melody from this period will consist of balanced
groups of measures, and although the Classical composer often disrupted the basic regularity of his phrases by extension or contraction, one is still correct in considering regularity
as the norm.
   The following examples, consisting of melodic excerpts from many different periods in
Western music, are a fairly convincing argument for symmetry and balance.

Mauduit—*Qui dire seult comme l'amour pique*

Praetorius—*Jesus ist ein süsser Nam*

Bach—*Partita No. 1 for Unaccompanied Violin*

Mozart—*Symphony in G minor, K. 550.*

Ravel—*Ma Mère L'Oye*

When melody is combined with harmony its symmetry is further enhanced, for the chords, though they move with a rhythm of their own, normally serve to reinforce the balanced structure of the melody which they support.

The following two excerpts are taken from the music of the Classical period. They are extremely simple in nature, but there is much to be learned from them.

Haydn—*Symphony No. 94, in G major*

54

roots

Melodically considered, the regularity of both excerpts is obvious. The Haydn example consists of three units of four measures with concluding unit of six measures—a deliberate extension of the phrase to emphasize the harmonic destination of D major. The Beethoven example is even more regular and consists simply of two units of four measures.

Considered from the standpoint of harmonic rhythm, the regularity is even more pronounced, and a close look at the harmonic roots which have been written in below the melodies reveals clearly a succession of units of two measures or, more broadly viewed, of four measures.

The harmonic vocabulary of both excerpts is surprisingly limited: the Haydn example uses I, II, IV, and V, and the Beethoven example uses I, VI, II, and V. Tonal-degree triads predominate in both cases.

The last but not least important observation concerns the root movement involved, and in both cases it is almost exclusively root movement of a descending fifth.

THE BEGINNING OF THE PHRASE

Although a phrase normally begins with the tonic chord, it may equally well avoid this immediate tonic emphasis by beginning with a different chord or series of chords. There are many ways in which the tonic chord may be postponed; the following example presents some common possibilities.

The three preceding progressions are similar in one important respect: they are each based on root movement of a descending fifth. The supertonic triad is frequently altered chromatically to become VofV, and the submediant triad may be altered chromatically to become VofII. These chromatic alterations, by referring to other dominants, add to rather than detract from the strength of the progressions.

EXERCISES

1. Given the following harmonic skeletons, make four-part settings in close position:

(a) in C major (with E as the first note in the soprano)

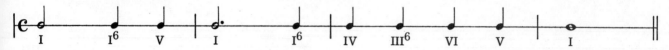

I   I⁶   V   I   I⁶   IV   III⁶   VI   V   I

(b) in G major (with D as the first note in the soprano)

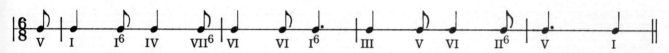

V   I   I⁶   IV   VII⁶ VI   VI   I⁶   III   V   VI   II⁶   V   I

(c) in D minor (with D as the first note in the soprano)

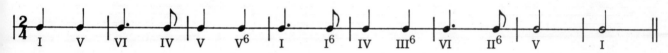

I   V   VI   IV   V   V⁶   I   I⁶   IV   III⁶   VI   II⁶   V   I

(d) in A minor (with E as the first note in the soprano)

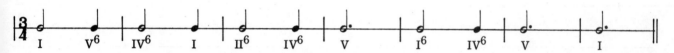

I   V⁶   IV⁶   I   II⁶   IV⁶   V   I⁶   IV⁶   V   I

(e) in E major (with B as the first note in the soprano)

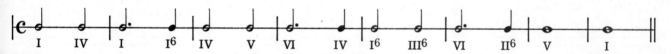

I   IV   I   I⁶   IV   V   VI   IV   I⁶   III⁶   VI   II⁶   V   I

(f) in F minor (with C as the first note in the soprano)

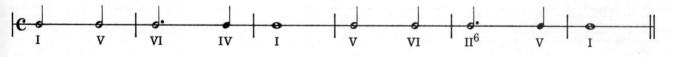

I   V   VI   IV   I   V   VI   II⁶   V   I

2. Given the following harmonic skeletons, make four-part settings in open position:

(a) in C minor (with C as the first note in the soprano)

(b) in E-flat major (with B-flat as the first note in the soprano)

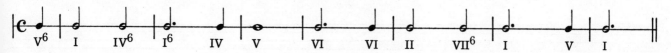

V⁶   I   IV⁶   I⁶   IV   V   VI   VI   II   VII⁶   I   V   I

(c) in B-flat major (with C as the first note in the soprano)

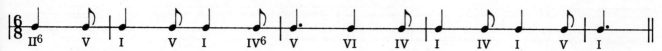

II⁶   V   I   V   I   IV⁶   V   VI   IV   I   IV   I   V   I

(d) in F-sharp minor (with A as the first note in the soprano)

VI   II⁶   V   I   I⁶   IV   IV⁶   I

(e) in C-sharp minor (with E as the first note in the soprano)

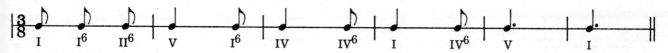

I   I⁶   II⁶   V   I⁶   IV   IV⁶   I   IV⁶   V   I

(f) in B major (with B as the first note in the soprano)

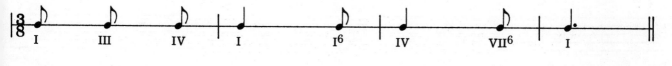

I   III   IV   I   I⁶   IV   VII⁶   I

3. STUDY AND ANALYSIS

Derive the rhythmic pattern of the roots of the harmony from each of the following phrases, which are taken from the music of the common-practice period. Upon each of these patterns, construct musically interesting four-part settings in open position.

Accidentals in the original phrases are to be ignored because they refer to chords and procedures in advance of the present stage of study. The texture should be a simple, vocal one, with stress on stepwise motion and no rests in any of the voices.

The result, from the standpoint of texture, will not be as interesting as the original phrase. This exercise, however, is concerned with harmonic progression and not with style.

(a) Beethoven—*Piano Sonata No. 4, op. 7*: third movement, measures 1 through 8

(b) Beethoven—*Piano Sonata No. 7, op. 10 No. 3*: third movement, measures 1 through 16

(c) Bach—*The Well-Tempered Clavier*, Book I: Prelude XVII, measure 1 through the first quarter note of measure 9

(d)   Bach—*The Well-Tempered Clavier*, Book I: Prelude XXI, measure 1 through the
first quarter note of measure 3

VII / HARMONIZATION OF A GIVEN PART

Required Reading: Piston, Chapter 7.

All the knowledge so far gained is called into play in the harmonization of a given part. But before the student sinks beneath the weight of his own erudition, he should understand that certain considerations are more important than others.

It is most important that the voices of the exercise have some independence and interest as lines. The inner voices will necessarily be somewhat limited in their activity; the outer voices, being freer, should be carefully worked out.

Equal in importance with the independence of the voices is the question of root progression and root emphasis. No melody can survive a harmonization that emphasizes root movement of a third or emphasizes modal-degree triads. The strength of a melody is directly related to the roots which support it. Study of the music of the common-practice period will show that the root movement most strongly emphasized is root movement of a fifth, that the triads most strongly emphasized are tonal-degree triads.

The last consideration is doubling. The student should be aware of the fact that certain doublings strengthen the chord and the tonality while other doublings weaken them. But he will find in his experience that both voice leading and root progression will take precedence over this last consideration.

The following statements should be of some help in the harmonization of a given part.

(1) A phrase normally begins and ends with root-position triads because they have more strength than their inversions;

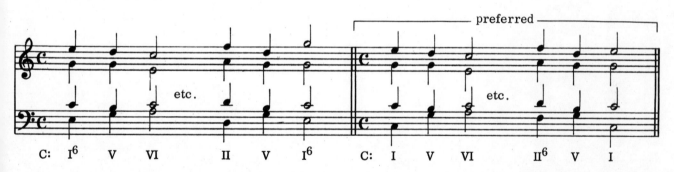

(2) the harmonization of a given part should consist of a balanced use of root-position triads and chords of the sixth; exclusive use of root-position triads results in a poor bass, and exclusive use of chords of the sixth creates a somewhat ambiguous harmonic structure;

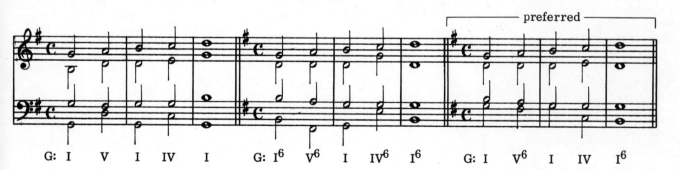

(3) two, and sometimes three, successive notes of a given melody or bass may be harmonized by a single chord, provided the chord does not enter on the last beat of the measure and cross over the bar line;

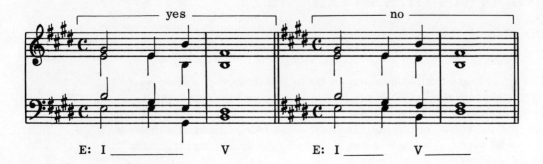

(4) a chord entering on a weak beat of the measure should not be held through the succeeding strong beat unless the resultant harmonic syncopation is deliberately intended.

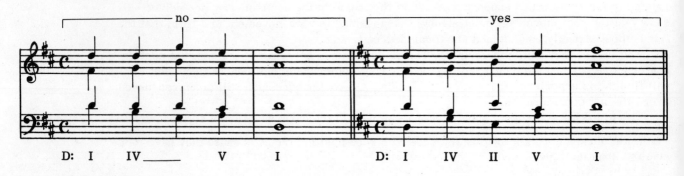

EXERCISES

1. Harmonize the following melodic fragments in close position, using root position triads only:

C major _____

Play fragment (A) in G, D, and A major;

Play fragment (B) in E, B, and F-sharp major;

Play fragment (C) in D-flat, A-flat, and E-flat major;

Play fragment (D) in B-flat, F, and G major;

Play fragment (E) in D, A, and E major;

Play fragment (F) in G, E, and F major.

2. Harmonize the following melodic fragments in close position, using root-position triads only:

A minor _____

Play fragment (A) in G, E, and F minor;

Play fragment (B) in D, A, and E minor;

Play fragment (C) in B-flat, F, and G minor;

Play fragment (D) in C-sharp, G-sharp, and E-flat minor;

Play fragment (E) in E, B, and F-sharp minor;

Play fragment (F) in G, D, and A minor.

3. Harmonize the following melodic fragments in open position, using root-position triads and chords of the sixth:

C major _____

Play fragment (A) in G and D major;

Play fragment (B) in A and E major;

Play fragment (C) in B and G-flat major;

Play fragment (D) in B-flat and F major.

4. Harmonize the following melodic fragments in open position, using root-position triads and chords of the sixth:

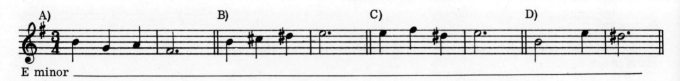

E minor

Note: When a melody or a bass, in the minor mode, ascends stepwise from the dominant to the tonic or descends stepwise from the tonic to the dominant, the melodic form of the scale will of course be used and will inevitably affect the harmony.

d: I⁶   IV   VII⁶   I   III   IV   V

Play fragment (A) in C and G minor;

Play fragment (B) in D and A minor;

Play fragment (C) in B and F-sharp minor;

Play fragment (D) in B-flat and F minor.

5. Harmonize the following melodies in open position, using root-position triads and chords of the sixth:

D major

G major

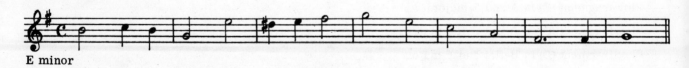

E♭ major

E minor

6. Harmonize the following basses in open position, using root-position triads and chords of the sixth:

Note: it must be constantly kept in mind that good voice leading is more important than "correct" doubling and that the voices, to move well as well as to double correctly, will frequently change from one position to the other.

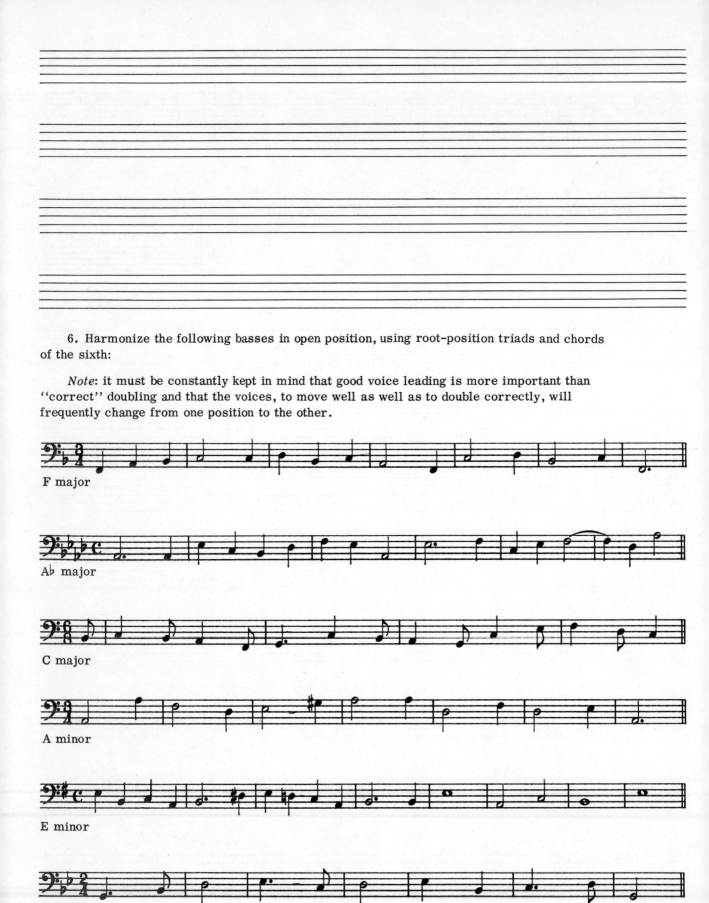

F major

A♭ major

C major

A minor

E minor

G minor

7. Make two four-part settings in open position of the following melody. The first setting should be in G major and end with an authentic cadence; the second setting should be in E minor and end with a half cadence.

Make two four-part settings in open position of the following melody. The first setting should be in F major and end with a plagal cadence; the second setting should be in D minor and end with a half cadence.

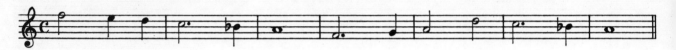

Make two four-part settings in open position of the following melody. The first setting should be in B major and end with an authentic cadence; the second setting should be in G-sharp minor and end with a half cadence.

Make two four-part settings in open position of the following melody. The first setting should be in E-flat major and end with a plagal cadence; the second setting should be in C minor and end with a half cadence.

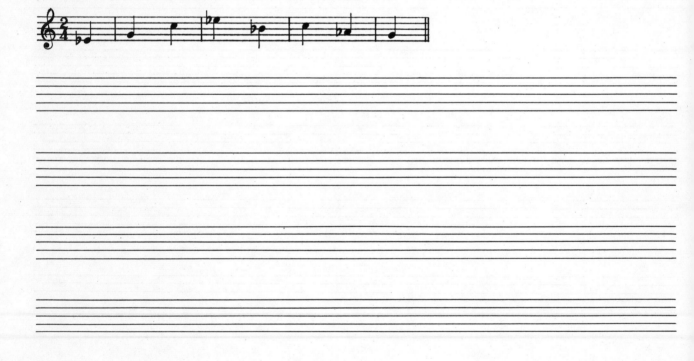

70

8. STUDY AND ANALYSIS

The following examples are suggested for study, with specific attention to be given to phrase length, to the triads and the particular root movement emphasized within the phrase, and to the nature of the bass line and its intervallic relation to the melody:

Schubert—*Die schöne Müllerin*:

1. *Das Wandern*, in its entirety;

4. *Danksagung an den Bach*, measure 1 through the first quarter note of measure 18;

11. *Mein!*, measures 1 through 21;

16. *Die liebe Farbe*, in its entirety.

VIII / NONHARMONIC TONES

Required reading: Piston, Chapter 8.

    Up to this point, the melodies used for harmonization have consisted exclusively of chordal tones. And although this limitation had, for a time, a pedagogical value, the fact must be recognized that melody in the common-practice period almost always involves notes that are a departure from or elaboration of its basic structure, notes that often conflict with the supporting harmony.

    The extent of melodic elaboration is fundamentally a question of style and period. Melody in the late Baroque period was often extraordinarily ornate; melody in the Classical period, on the other hand, tended toward a clearer relation with the underlying harmony.

    The following examples, even without harmonic analysis, should make the difference quite apparent.

Bach—*St. John Passion*

Haydn—*The Creation*

    The student, when faced with these somewhat extreme examples, may wonder just how extensively he should use nonharmonic tones in his written work. The answer is: with moderation. Whether the nonharmonic tones are limited to the melody or extend to other voices as well, the fact remains that too much elaboration results in "fussiness" and blurs the harmony. In the following example, nonharmonic tones are present in two voices at the same time, but never in more. This is an arbitrary limitation but a practical one, and should be observed.

basic scheme

elaboration

VOICE LEADING

The use of nonharmonic tones complicates the harmonic texture, and for this reason the problem of parallel fifths and octaves must be looked at again. It is fortunately not as complicated as one might suspect and can be reduced to the following prohibitions:

(1) parallel fifths and octaves should be avoided between successive strong beats, or more precisely, between successive accented notes:

(2) parallel fifths and octaves should be avoided between adjacent notes:

There are exceptions to every rule. One can find, in the harmonized chorales of Bach, examples of parallel fifths between successive accented notes as well as between adjacent notes. But since parallel fifths and octaves are never absolutely necessary or inevitable, the simple answer to the problems which they create is to avoid them.

NONHARMONIC TONES IN THE MINOR MODE

Certain melodies, because of their supporting roots, will violate the normal usage of the melodic minor scale.

In Example 156, in the required reading for this chapter, the sixth and seventh degree of the scale proceed in a normal manner.

If they proceed in a normal manner in the following example, however, the result will be a minor dominant triad and a major subdominant triad. The normal usage of the scale is violated in favor of keeping the dominant triad major and the subdominant triad minor.

74

wrong   right

c: V   I⁶   IV_____   V   I⁶   IV_____

OBSERVATIONS

The required reading for this chapter more than adequately describes the character and function of the different nonharmonic tones. A few selected observations may, however, help the student in his written work:

(1) if two voices using passing tones move in similar motion, they will move in parallel thirds or sixths;

(2) if two voices using auxiliary tones move in similar motion, they will move in parallel thirds or sixths;

(3) if the appoggiatura appears in the alto, tenor, or the bass, the note of resolution should not appear in any other voice;

yes

or

(4) a tied note can be considered a suspension only if it is a dissonant note that demands resolution.

suspensions

not suspensions

EXERCISES

1. Play progression (A) in G, D, A, E, and B major;

   Play progression (B) in E, G, D, F, and C minor;

   Play progression (C) in A, C, G, B-flat, and F major.

A) C major

B) A minor

C) D major

2. Add nonharmonic tones to the following progressions where they will work well:

(1) C minor (2) (3)

(4)

E♭ major

(5)

E♭ major

(6)

E♭ major

3. Harmonize the following melodies in open position, using root-position triads and chords of the sixth. Add nonharmonic tones where they will work well, but leave the soprano as it is.

G major

A minor

A major

G minor

(V)

D major

D minor

4. Harmonize the following basses in open position, using root-position triads and chords of the sixth. Add nonharmonic tones where they will work well, but leave the bass as it is.

Bb major

G minor

F major

D minor

(V)

5. STUDY AND ANALYSIS

The following excerpts are suggested for study with particular attention to be paid to the nonharmonic tones involved:

Bach—*The Well-Tempered Clavier*, Book I:

Prelude II, measure 1 through 9;

Prelude V, measure 1 through the first quarter note of measure 10;

Prelude VI, measure 1 through the first quarter note of measure 6;

Prelude XI, measure 1 through the first dotted quarter note of measure 8;

Prelude XX, measure 1 through the first dotted quarter note of measure 5;

Prelude XXIV, measure 1 through the first half note of measure 12.

IX / THE SIX-FOUR CHORD

Required reading: Piston, Chapter 9.

RHYTHMIC DIFFERENCES

The four kinds of six-four chord reveal the following difference in regard to accent: the cadential and appoggiatura six-four chords fall on a strong beat of the measure, while the auxiliary and passing six-four chords fall on a weak beat of the measure.

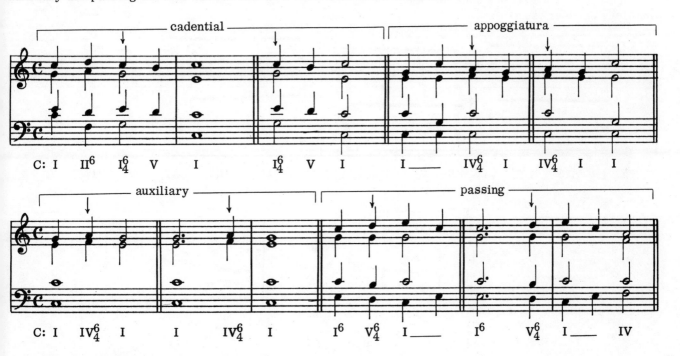

VOICE LEADING

It will be further observed that the tone common to the six-four chord and the chord which follows it is retained by the same voice, or voices, and that two of the voices normally move in parallel thirds or sixths (see above example again).

USES OF THE SIX-FOUR CHORD

Although the cadential six-four chord is always a tonic six-four chord, the appoggiatura, auxiliary, and passing six-four chords may be constructed on other degrees of the scale as well as on the tonic, and the following is a list of common possibilities:

appoggiatura six-four chord: I, II, IV, and VI in a major key,
I, IV, and VI in a minor key;

auxiliary six-four chord: I, II, IV, and VI in a major key,
I, IV, and VI in a minor key;

passing six-four chord: I and V in a major key, V in a minor key.

Appoggiatura six-four chord

C: IV$_4^6$ I I^6 I$_4^6$ V___ II$_4^6$ VI___ VI$_4^6$ III   c: IV$_4^6$ I VI VI$_4^6$ III IV I$_4^6$ V I

Auxiliary six-four chord

C: I IV$_4^6$ I V VI II$_4^6$ VI____ III VI$_4^6$ III_____ V I$_4^6$ V

c: I IV$_4^6$ I VI III VI$_4^6$ III IV V I$_4^6$ V V$_5^6$ I

Passing six-four chord

C: I V$_4^6$ I^6 IV I$_4^6$ IV^6 I$_4^6$ V___ I   c: I V$_4^6$ I^6 II^6 I$_4^6$ V I

EXERCISES

1. Play progression (A) in G, D, A, and E major;

   Play progression (B) in C, F, B-flat, and D major;

   Play progression (C) in A, E, B, and C minor;

   Play progression (D) in G, C, F, and B-flat major.

(A)

C major

(B)

G major

(C)

D minor

(D)

E major

2. Harmonize the following melodies in open position, using six-four chords where indicated by an asterisk (*):

F major

F minor

Bb major

G major

3. Harmonize the following basses in open position, using six-four chords where indicated by an asterisk (*);

A minor

Eb major

B major

C minor

passing tone

4. STUDY AND ANALYSIS

The following excerpts and complete compositions are suggested for study, with specific attention to be given to six-four chords, to their kind and their placement in the measure:

Beethoven—*String Quartet, op. 18, No. 1*: third movement, measures 17 through 29, as well as measures 122 through 138;

String Quartet, op. 131: second movement, measures 1 through 16;

String Quartet, op. 132: fifth movement, measures 1 through 18.

Schubert—*Die schöne Müllerin*:

XI. *Mein!*
XVI. *Die liebe Farbe*;
XIX. *Der Müller und der Bach*;
XX. *Des Baches Wiegenlied*.

X / CADENCES

Required reading: Piston, Chapter 10.

THE AUTHENTIC CADENCE

The authentic cadence consists of the progression V–I. When both chords appear in root position with the tonic degree in the soprano at the end, the cadence is considered perfect. When inversions are used or when the soprano in the tonic chord uses the third or fifth rather than the root of the triad, the cadence, then considered imperfect, has less weight and less finality.

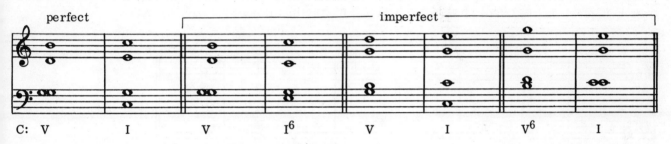

The authentic cadence is ordinarily preceded by IV, II, or II⁶.

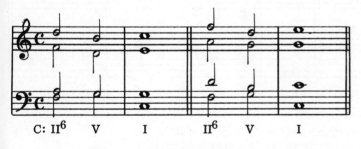

If a cadential six-four chord is added to the cadence, it should, of course, fall on a strong beat of the measure.

THE PLAGAL CADENCE

The plagal cadence consists of the progression IV-I, and the distinction between perfect and imperfect applies to this cadence as well as to the authentic cadence. It is often preceded by an authentic cadence, and the combination of these four chords with their concentration on tonal-degree triads gives it a weight and finality that it does not have by itself.

THE HALF CADENCE

If the authentic and plagal cadences may be considered the period in the harmonic sentence, the half cadence is clearly the semicolon. It is a temporary, rather than a final, point of rest. The half cadence moves from I, I^6, II, II^6, IV, IV^6, or VI to the dominant chord. Like the authentic cadence, it may include a cadential six-four chord.

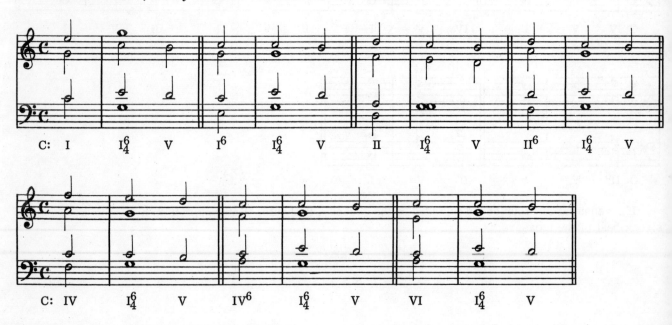

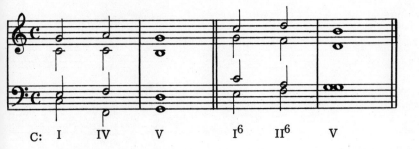

C: I   IV   V   I⁶   II⁶   V

THE DECEPTIVE CADENCE

If the dominant chord in a cadential situation resolves not to the tonic but to some other chord, the cadence is considered deceptive. The possibilities for "evading" the tonic are various; two common alternatives are the resolution to VI or to IV⁶.

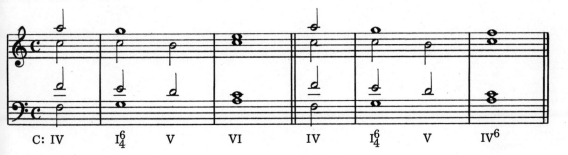

C: IV   I⁶₄   V   VI   IV   I⁶₄   V   IV⁶

EXERCISES

1. Make a four-part setting in open position of the following cadences:

Play cadence (A) in E-flat, F-sharp, A, and D-flat major;

Play cadence (B) in B-flat, D-flat, E, and A-flat major;

Play cadence (C) in F, A-flat, B, and E-flat major;

Play cadence (D) in C, E-flat, F-sharp, and B-flat minor;

Play cadence (E) in G, B-flat, C-sharp, and F minor;

Play cadence (F) in D, F, G-sharp, and C minor.

2. Harmonize the following melodies in open position, using triads in root position and in inversions. Nonharmonic tones do not figure prominently in the melodies and are to be used sparingly in the other voices.

3. Harmonize the following basses in open position, using triads in root position and in inversions. Nonharmonic tones are not present in the basses and are to be used sparingly in the other voices.

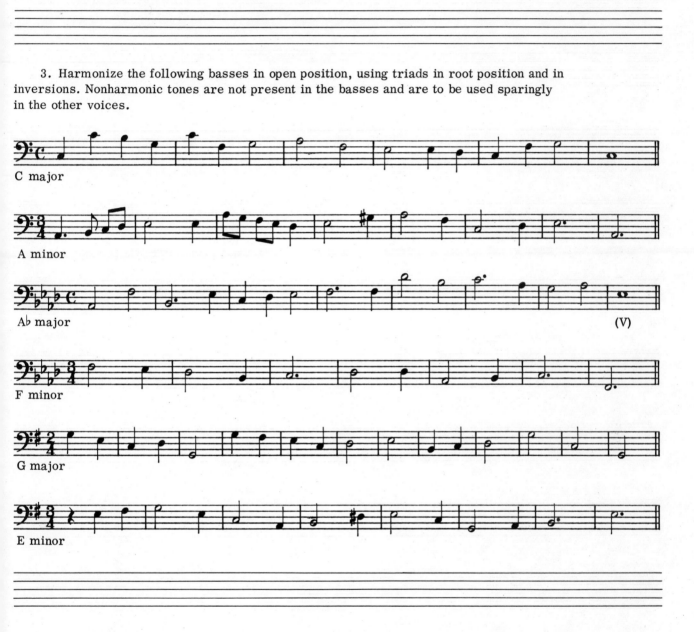

4. STUDY AND ANALYSIS

The following cadential excerpts are suggested for study and analysis:

Bach—*French Suite No. 1 in D minor*:

Courante, measures 9 and 10;
Sarabande, measures 23 and 24;
Minuet I, measures 23 and 24;
Minuet II, measures 15 and 16.

Beethoven—*Piano Sonata No. 1, op. 2, No. 1*: first movement, measures 7 and 8;

Piano Sonata No. 1, op. 2, No. 1: second movement, measures 15 and 16;

Piano Sonata No. 3, op. 2, No. 3: first movement, measures 212 through 220;

Piano Sonata No. 3, op. 2, No. 3: second movement, measures 9 through 11.

Bach—*The Well-Tempered Clavier*, Book I:

Prelude X, measures 35 through 41;
Prelude XVII, measures 41 through 44.

XI / HARMONIC RHYTHM

Required reading: Piston, Chapter 11.

Melody and harmony, in the music of the common-practice period, are distinct, yet deeply related musical elements. In some types of composition, such as the Baroque fugue, attention is focused strongly upon the individual voices, and harmony is the product of these moving voices.

Bach—*Partita No. 5*: *Gigue*

In contrast to the Baroque fugue, music such as Romantic lieder is clearly harmonic in nature; the melody, in this body of literature, is almost invariably the outgrowth of a succession of chords.

Schubert—*Winterreise*: *Einsamkeit*

Wie ei - ne trü - be_ Wol - ke durch hei - t're Lüf - te_ geht,   wenn

Regardless of which element may predominate in a particular piece of music, however, both harmony and melody will be present and both will play an active role in the musical motion, for each element has a rhythmic aspect.

In music of an extremely simple texture where all of the voices coincide, the melodic and harmonic rhythms will be almost identical.

Schumann—*Symphonic Etudes, op. 13*

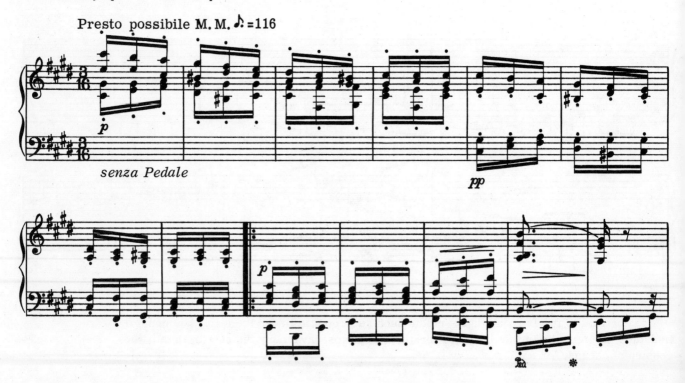

In music of an elaborate texture, the activity of the voices will tend to obscure the underlying motion from one chord to another, and the harmonic rhythm, as a result, will play a secondary role.

Bach—*Musical Offering: Ricercar a 6*

Somewhere in between these two extremes lies most of the music of the common-practice period, music in which the rhythm of one element complements and enhances the rhythm of the other, music which is a balance between the two. The following excerpt is a representative example of this balance.

Bach—*French Suite No. 5: Courante*

THE RHYTHMIC TEXTURE OF MUSIC

The required reading on this subject clearly describes the nature and function of the two kinds of rhythm, melodic and harmonic. At the same time, some amplifying remarks may be in order regarding harmonic rhythm, for it is indeed a difficult and subtle subject.

Certain chords in a musical phrase are more important than others, and their importance is directly related to the degrees of the scale upon which they are built. There can be no question that tonal-degree triads establish and solidify the key and that these same triads, used in a cadence, define and punctuate the phrase.

When rhythm enters into consideration, the harmonic activity receives an added dimension. One must then say that the importance of a chord does not depend simply upon its root, but is determined by several other factors: (1) its duration; (2) the root relationship to its neighboring chords; (3) the presence or absence of dissonance; and (4) its placement in the measure.

A musical phrase will consist of a number of different chords. The frequency with which harmonies change is a completely flexible matter and varies from one composition to another. One can say, however, that the extremes are the exceptions, that very few phrases will consist of only one harmony or of continual harmonic change.

In a phrase consisting of a number of different chords, some chords will be held longer than others. There can be no questioning the fact that long time values are rhythmically strong, while short time values are rhythmically weak. Or, in other words, that the duration of a chord has a definite effect on its rhythmic weight and importance.

Brahms—*Rapsodie, op. 119, No. 4*

Allegro risoluto

A next consideration in regard to harmonic rhythm is the inherent rhythmic value of the harmonic progression. Although no conclusive statements can be made in this area, one can say that progressions in which the root moves up or down a fifth or by step are strong progressions, and in these progressions the rhythmic weight falls on the second chord.

Progressions in which the root moves up a third are weak progressions, while progressions in which the root moves down a third are neither strong nor weak.

A close analysis of the following excerpt should not only clarify the preceding statements but reveal both the difficulty and potentialities of this kind of interpretation.

The excerpt is presented first as a succession of chords with neither time signature nor bar lines.

Considered purely from the standpoint of root movement, some chords will have more rhythmic weight than others. The subtlety of this kind of interpretation is all too clear when one realizes that within the group of strong chords, some are stronger than others. Harmony, after all, does not consist of isolated progressions, but of a series of interrelated chords.

The next, and final, step is the introduction of bar lines to group the chords in a regular manner and to indicate, by their placement, where the strongly accented harmonies fall.

Two different barrings are presented here. The first barring conflicts with the inherent rhythmic character of the harmonic progressions; the second barring—the actual barring of the Bach chorale—heightens them.

Bach—*Gelobet seist du, Jesu Christ*

Although most dissonance is melodic in origin, there are some chords that contain within themselves a dissonant interval and demand a resolution of the tension which they create. These chords are augmented and diminished triads and chords of the seventh.

When one of these chords resolves in a normal manner by root movement of a descending fifth, the result is a strong progression, from the standpoint of harmonic rhythm, and the combination of a strong progression with dissonance in the first chord gives to the chord of resolution a definite feeling of "arrival," regardless of where the progression falls in the measure.

Haydn—*The Lady's Looking-Glass*

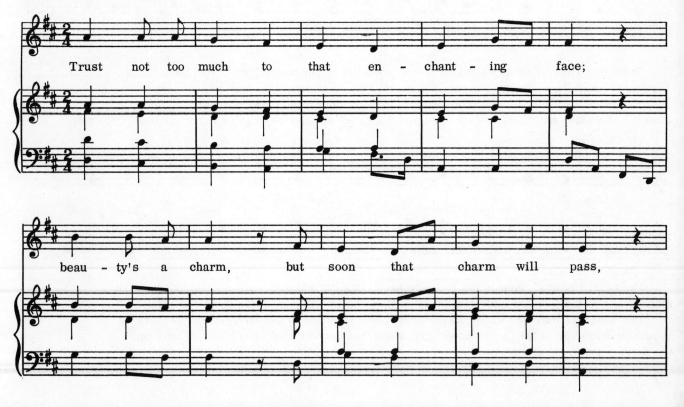

Trust not too much to that en - chant - ing face;

beau - ty's a charm, but soon that charm will pass,

When the agogic element conflicts with the symmetry of the measure and its conventionalized division into strong and weak beats, the result is syncopation. And syncopation is nothing more than the appearance of long time values in unexpected places in the measure.

Syncopation can be employed in three different ways: it can be purely melodic, purely harmonic, or it can involve both elements. The following example should illustrate the three possibilities and at the same time reveal the rhythmic importance of this device.

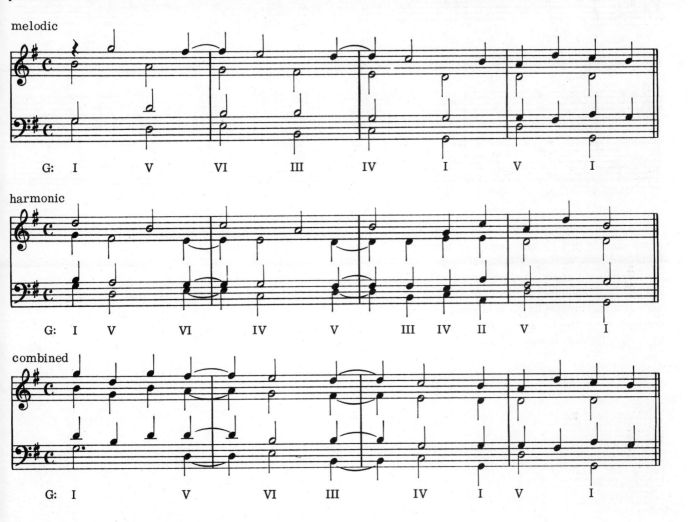

TEMPO AND HARMONIC ANALYSIS

Although the placement of a chord in the measure is of relatively little importance in comparison to its duration and its root relationship to its neighbors, the question of its functional nature is most definitely related to the question of weak and strong beats as well as to tempo.

As an example, a six-four chord in a slow tempo will be recognized as a distinct harmony; in a fast tempo, however, it may be less a distinct harmony and more the result of auxiliary or passing tones. A logical extension of this observation is the idea of passing chords, auxiliary chords, and appoggiatura chords.

Largo

e: I   IV$_4^6$ I   V^6_____   I   IV^6 I$_4^6$ V

Vivace

e: I   VI   II^6 V_____   (I$_4^6$)_____   6   I_____

As his analytical experience grows, the student of harmony will begin to realize that some chords in a phrase are more important than others, and that their importance is determined by a variety of factors.

Harmonic analysis is, after all, not simply a matter of objective measurement, but a seriously thought-out process of evaluation. A telling illustration lies in the fact that one aspect of harmony—its rhythm—cannot be understood in its fullest sense without taking into consideration the following: duration, root relationship, dissonance, placement in the measure, and, finally, tempo.

EXERCISES

1. Harmonize each of the following melodies in open position in two different ways:
(a) with few changes of harmony; and (b) with several changes of harmony.

2. Harmonize the following basses in open position, using syncopation in the melody:

3. Harmonize the following melodies in open position, using syncopation in the harmony:

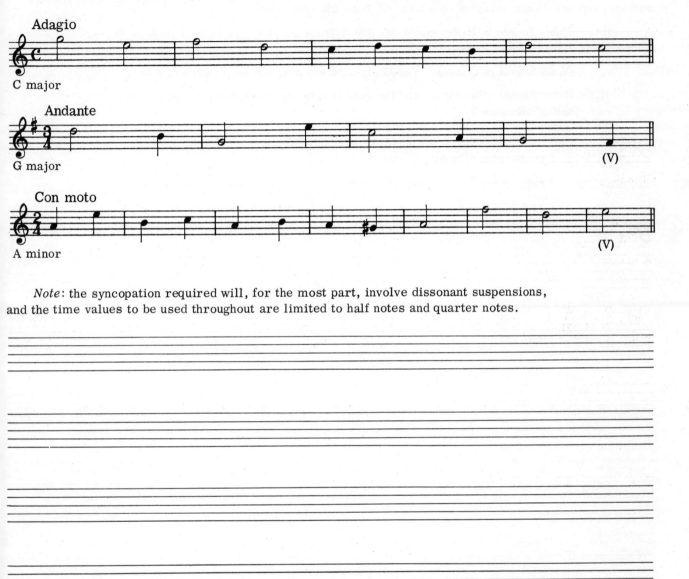

Note: the syncopation required will, for the most part, involve dissonant suspensions, and the time values to be used throughout are limited to half notes and quarter notes.

4. Determine the harmonic rhythm of, and chords involved in, the following phrases, and make new four-part settings in open position.

Retain the metre, tempo, and key of the original phrase; but, though the new setting should follow the original succession of roots, the question of root position versus inversion is left entirely up to the individual.

Any particular harmony may be rhythmically enlivened by shifting from one position to another, and non-harmonic tones may be used, but with moderation.

Mozart—*Piano Sonata in B-flat major, K. 333*: third movement, measure 1 through the first half of measure 9;

Piano Sonata in C major, K. 545: first movement, measures 1 through 8;

Piano Sonata in D major, K. 576: third movement, measure 1 through the first half of measure 9.

Beethoven—*Piano Sonata No. 1, op. 2, No. 1*: second movement, measure 1 through the first quarter note of measure 9;

Piano Sonata No. 2, op. 2, No. 2: second movement, measures 1 through 8;

Piano Sonata No. 5, op. 10, No. 1: second movement, measure 1 through the first half of measure 10.

5. Make two different four-part settings in close position of each of the following chordal series. Although each of the settings does not have to be completely different, each pair of settings should offer contrast in terms of time signature and harmonic rhythm. The question of root position versus inversion is left entirely up to the individual, and the tempo of each setting should be thought of as moderate.

(a) I-IV-V-VI-II-V-I-VI-IV-II-V-I (in D major);

(b) I-III-IV-V-I-II-V-VI-IV-I (in F minor);

(c) I-VI-V-I-VII-I-IV-I-III-VI-V-I-IV-V-I (in A-flat major).

6. Make two different harmonic clothings of each of the following rhythmic patterns. The question of key, mode, and chord position is left entirely up to the individual. All six settings should be in open position and should end with a tonic chord. The tempo of each setting should be thought of as moderate.

(a)

(b)

(c)

XII / MODULATION

Required reading: Piston, Chapter 12.

THE INITIAL KEY

In establishing a key, it is the dominant, rather than the tonic, which is most important. A succession of chords without dominant harmony, which is to say without V or its related triad VII, may suggest the key, but will almost invariably rely too heavily on modal-degree triads.

G: I   VI   III   VI   I⁶   IV   IV⁶   I

It is the presence of V or VII that establishes the key in a truly convincing and strong manner. And only after a key has been firmly established is the music free to modulate.

Bach—*An Wasserflüssen Babylon*

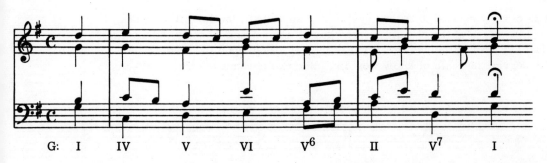

G: I   IV   V   VI   V⁶   II   V⁷   I

The importance of dominant harmony in the music of the common-practice period is nowhere more clearly revealed than in the harmonized chorales of Bach. The student is well-advised to study as many of these chorales as he can. He will discover that in almost all the chorales the initial key is established by the presence of its dominant.

THE NEW KEY

In the following example, a melody, modulating from G major to D major, has been harmonized in two different ways: (1) without dominant harmony, and (2) with dominant harmony. In the first harmonization the initial and the new keys are established, at least to some extent, by the presence of the two leading-tone degrees (F-sharp and C-sharp). In the second harmonization the initial and the new keys are strongly established, and this is entirely due to the presence of their respective dominants.

G: I I IV$_4^6$ I III^6 VI II^6 I I   D: {I / IV _____ III^6 VI II^6 I

G: I I IV V III^6 VI V^6 I I   D: {I / IV II I^6 VI II^6 V I

RELATED KEYS

Any two keys can be joined by modulation, but some keys are more closely related than others. The degree of relationship between keys is determined by the amount of chromatic change necessary to move into the new key.

The modulation from C major to G major requires only one chromatic change: F-sharp. The two keys are closely related. The modulation from C major to A-flat major requires four chromatic changes. These two keys are more distantly related.

The question as to what keys are closely related can be answered by the following pair of statements:

(1) a major key is closely related to those keys which can be built on the different degrees of its scale, and the mode of the closely related key is determined by the triad as it is found in the original key. *Note*: the one exception is the key based upon the leading-tone degree. To make this degree the tonic of a key would require two chromatic changes (F-sharp and C-sharp).

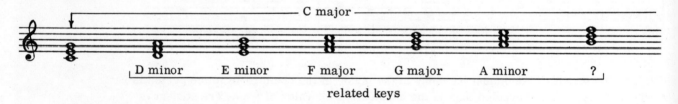

related keys

(2) a minor key is closely related to those keys which can be built on the different degrees of its scale as it is "naturally" constituted without altering either the sixth or seventh degree, and the mode of the closely related key is determined by the triad as it is found in the original key. *Note*: the one exception is the key based upon the supertonic degree. To make this degree the tonic of a key would require two chromatic changes (E-natural and A-natural).

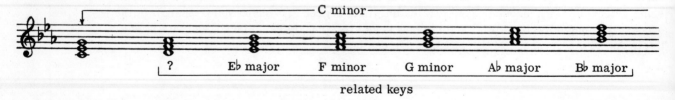

related keys

A table of closely related keys, limited to C as the tonality, is as follows:

C major: D minor, E minor, F major, G major, and A minor.

C minor: E-flat major, F minor, G minor, A-flat major, and B-flat major.

In summary, closely related keys are those which require one or no chromatic change to move from the key signature of the first key to the key signature of the second.

THE PIVOT CHORD

Two closely related keys have always more than one chord in common.

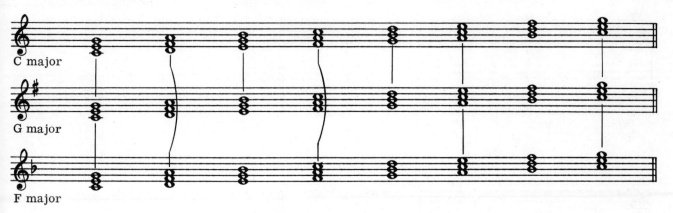

C major

G major

F major

As a result of this fact of common chords, a modulation from one key to another closely related to it is often a process of "overlapping" of keys; and from the standpoint of harmonic analysis, it is sometimes difficult to decide at what precise point the phrase has definitely moved into the new key. Until the dominant chord, or at least the leading-tone degree, has made its appearance, the modulation has not really been effected.

In working out a modulating phrase, however, it is not simply a matter of moving directly to the dominant of the new key. The initial key must first be firmly established before any modulation is possible. After this, the phrase, arriving at a chord common to both keys, begins to "think" in the new key. This "thinking" always involves cadential formulae, and particularly the authentic cadence.

In regard to closely related keys, there are always at least three chords common to both keys that can serve as pivots. The following example consists of modulations from C major to all of the closely related keys, and each of the modulations is achieved by means of a different pivot chord. These modulations are by no means the only ones possible; certainly every musical problem has many solutions. They will have served their purpose, however, if they call attention to the following facts:

(1) the dominant of the initial key is almost always present;

(2) the dominant of the new key is always present;

(3) the root movement following the pivot chord is primarily root movement of a fifth.

C: I   IV   V   I⁶
         G: {IV⁶   II⁶   I⁶₄   V   I

INTERCHANGEABILITY OF MODE

The nineteenth-century composer, in his search for new harmonic color, often modulated by means of a modal "shift." One of the most common procedures was a modulation from a major key to another major key a third above or below.

From the standpoint of closely related keys, such modulations are impossible. If a phrase modulates from C major to a key a third above or below it, the keys will be E minor or A minor. How can a modulation from C major to E major, or from C major to A major be achieved?

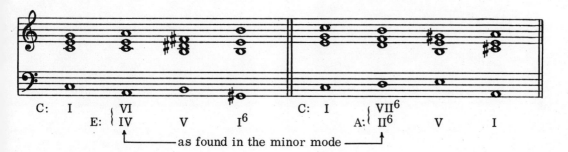

C: I   C: I

E: { VI / IV }   V   I⁶   A: { VII⁶ / II⁶ }   V   I

— as found in the minor mode —

If the pivot chord in a modulating phrase is "shifted" in mode, from the standpoint of either the initial or the new key, a world of new possibilities presents itself.

C: I { IV / Ab: VI } V   I   C: I { VI / Eb: IV } V   I⁶   C: I { II / A: IV } V   I   C: I { IV / Eb: II } V⁶   I

The examples so far presented by no means exhaust the possibilities. They do, however, reveal an important fact about modulation. As it moves to more distantly related keys and becomes more chromatic, the neat distinction between major and minor tends to disappear. And the result is a tonality which is a combination of both.

EXERCISES

1. Name the six closely related keys of each of the following: E major, G minor, B-flat major, C-sharp minor, F major, G-sharp minor, B major, and D minor.

2. Make a harmonic analysis of the following modulating phrases:

\=as found in the minor mode.

Play phrase (A) in G and D major;

Play phrase (B) in B-flat and F major;

Play phrase (C) in A and E major;

Play phrase (D) in A-flat and E-flat major;

Play phrase (E) in E-flat and B-flat minor;

Play phrase (F) in G and D minor;

Play phrase (G) in A and E minor;

Play phrase (H) in B and F-sharp minor;

Play phrase (I) in G major;

Play phrase (J) in D major;

Play phrase (K) in F major;

Play phrase (L) in B-flat major.

3. MAZES

Each of the mazes has two possible routes. Determine the chords involved for each of the routes, then make four-part settings in open position. Observe the harmonic rhythm specified above the maze and begin with the indicated scoring.

Note: III, in a minor key, is customarily an augmented triad, but may be a major triad if the seventh degree of the scale is used in its lowered form. This note of the triad will invariably descend. VII, customarily a diminished triad in a minor key, may be a major triad under the same condition.

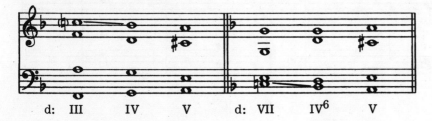

d: III   IV   V   d: VII   IV⁶   V

Modal "shift" is nowhere involved in these mazes.

C: I - IV⁶ - V⁶- I
```
           ⎡ VI
           ⎣ II  -  V⁶  -  ⎡ I
                          ⎣ IV  -  V - ⎡ I
  ⎡ VI                                ⎣ III  - II⁶ - I⁶₄ - V  -  I
  ⎣ IV  -  V  -  ⎡ I
               ⎣ II   -   V - ⎡ I
                             ⎣ IV  -  V - ⎡ I
                                         ⎣ III - IV  -  V
```

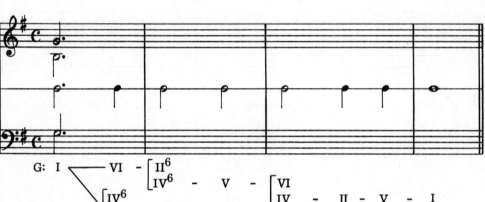

G: I
```
       ⎡ II⁶
  VI  - ⎣ IV⁶   -    V   -   ⎡ VI
                            ⎣ IV   -   II - V  -  I
  ⎡ IV⁶
  ⎣ I⁶  -  IV   -   VII⁶ ⎡ I
                        ⎣ III    -   II⁶ - V  -  I
```

D: ⎡ I
   ⎣ IV - V ⎡ I
             ⎣ III - IV - V   -   I - ⎡ I⁶
              I - V - ⎡ VI   ⎣ III⁶   -   VI - V - I
                      ⎣ I   -   V - V⁶   -   ⎡ I
                                             ⎣ VI - V - I

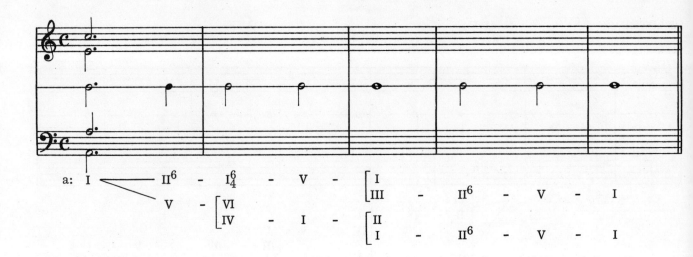

a: I ⟍ II^6 - I$^6_4$ - V - ⎡ I
  V - ⎡ VI   ⎣ III - II^6 - V - I
      ⎣ IV - I - ⎡ II
                  ⎣ I - II^6 - V - I

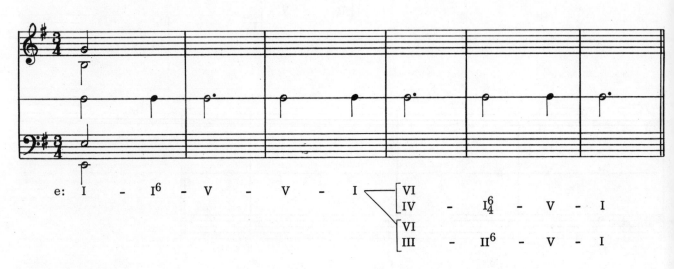

e: I - I^6 - V - V - I ⟍ ⎡ VI
                          ⎣ IV - I$^6_4$ - V - I
                          ⎡ VI
                          ⎣ III - II^6 - V - I

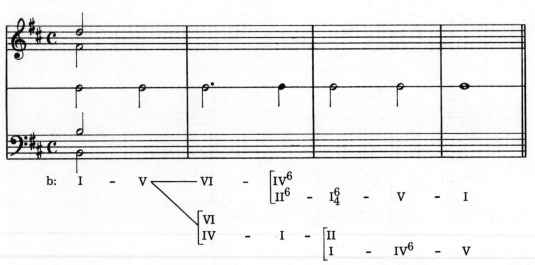

b: I - V ⟍ VI - ⎡ IV^6
                ⎣ II^6 - I$^6_4$ - V - I
          ⎡ VI
          ⎣ IV - I - ⎡ II
                      ⎣ I - IV^6 - V

128

4. Make two four-part settings in open position of each of the following melodies. The first setting should remain in the key, and the second setting should modulate to another key. The last chord of the melody may be either a tonic or a dominant chord.

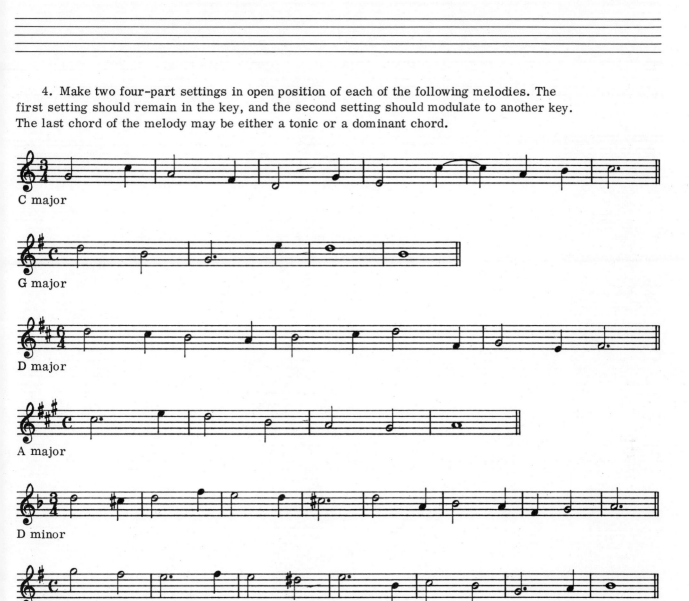

C major

G major

D major

A major

D minor

E minor

131

5. STUDY AND ANALYSIS

The following excerpts are suggested for study and complete harmonic analysis.

Bach—*Partita No. 6 in B-flat major*:
    Menuet I, measures 9 through 16.

Schumann—*Kreisleriana*:
>Intermezzo II, measures 1 through 8.

Beethoven—*String Quartet, op. 18, No. 5*:
>third movement, measures 1 through 8.

Bach—Chorale #54: *Lobt Gott, ihr Christen, allzugleich*:
>measure 1 through the first half note of measure 4.

Schubert—*Schwanengesang*:
>IV. *Ständchen*, measures 1 through 16.

Bach—*English Suite No. 2 in C minor*:
>*Menuet*, measures 1 through 8.

Bach—Chorale #349: *Ich hab' in Gottes Herz und Sinn*:
>measures 1 through 4.

Bach—Chorale #367: *Befiehl du deine Wege*:
>measures 1 through 4.

The following complete compositions are suggested for study and complete harmonic analysis.

Bach—Chorale #292: *Nimm von uns, Herr, du treuer Gott*.

Bach—*French Suite No. 5 in G major*:
>Gavotte.

XIII / THE DOMINANT SEVENTH CHORD

Required reading: Piston, Chapter 13.

ROOT POSITION AND INVERSION

The figured bass terminology for the dominant seventh chord in root position and inversion specifies the intervals formed by the root and seventh of the chord with the bass.

Root position: bass and root are the same note, bass and seventh form a seventh;

First inversion: bass and root form a sixth, bass and seventh form a fifth;

Second inversion: bass and root form a fourth, bass and seventh form a third;

Third inversion: bass and root form a second, bass and seventh are the same note.

It must be understood that the figured bass specifies only the bass note: the three other chord tones can be distributed in several different ways among the upper voices.

THE APPROACH TO THE DOMINANT SEVENTH CHORD

The dominant seventh chord may be preceded by I, II, III, IV, or VI. If it is preceded by V or VII, there is, in effect, no harmonic movement, for the dominant seventh chord is actually a combination of these two triads.

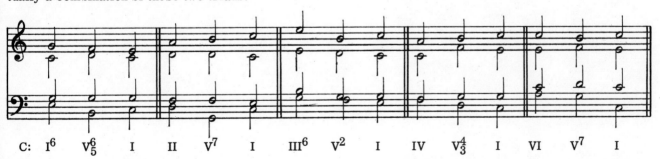

V_____   I   V_____   I

THE RESOLUTION OF THE DOMINANT SEVENTH CHORD

Considered from the standpoint of scale degrees, the regular resolution of the dominant seventh chord, whether in root position or in inversion, can be symbolized by the following figures: 4 to 3, and 7 to 8. Exceptions to this particular voice leading can indeed be found, and the student is referred to his required reading for a clear description of them.

Although the dominant seventh chord normally resolves to I, it may also resolve, in the manner of a deceptive cadence, to VI. It may also progress to IV and delay, in this way, the eventual resolution to I.

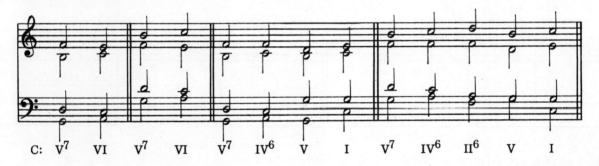

C: V⁷ VI   V⁷ VI   V⁷ IV⁶ V   I   V⁷ IV⁶ II⁶ V   I

EXERCISES

1. Make four-part settings in close position of the following melodic fragments:

C: I   II⁶   I⁶₄   V⁷   I   G: I   II⁶   I⁶₄   V⁷   VI   e: I   IV⁶   I⁶₄   V⁷   VI

D: V²   I⁶   V⁴₃   I   II⁶   I⁶₄   V⁷   IV⁶   IV   V⁷   I

b: V²   I⁶   V⁴₃   I   V⁷   VI   II⁶   V

Play fragment (A) in G and D major;

Play fragment (B) in D and A major;

Play fragment (C) in A and D minor;

Play fragment (D) in A and E major;

Play fragment (E) in F-sharp and C-sharp minor.

Compare your settings of fragments (A) and (B) with the different settings you made of them in Chapter 10.

2. Harmonize the following melodic fragments in open position, using dominant seventh chords where they will work well:

C major _____

A minor _____

Play each of these fragments in two different keys.

3. Harmonize the following melodies in open position, using dominant seventh chords where indicated by an asterisk (*):

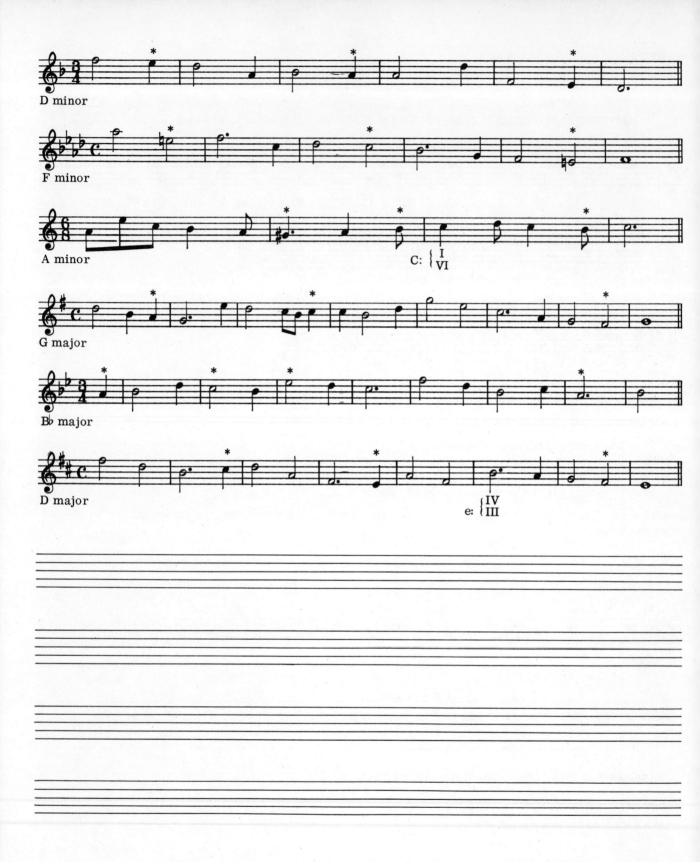

D minor

F minor

A minor

C: {I / VI}

G major

B♭ major

D major

e: {IV / III}

138

4. Given the following harmonic skeletons, make four-part settings in open position:

1. In C major (with B as the first note in the soprano)

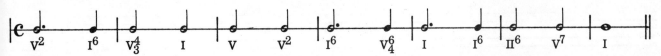

2. In A♭ -flat major (with D as the first note in the soprano)

V^2 I^6 V^6 I I^6 IV V_3^4 I V^6 I V^7 VI II^6 V^7 I

3. In G major (with B as the first note in the soprano)

I V_4^6 I^6 V_3^4 I^6 II^6 I_4^6 V^7 VI VI I^6 III^6 e [VI / I] IV^6 V^7 I

4. In A minor (with E as the first note in the soprano)

I V_5^6 I II^6 I_4^6 V^7 VI III II^6 V^7 I

5. In C minor (with E-flat as the first note in the soprano)

I IV^6 I^6 IV III^6 V^7 VI V V^2 I^6 I IV IV^6 I_4^6 V^7 I

6. In E minor (with B as the first note in the soprano)

I V_5^6 I V^2 I^6 V_3^4 I G {IV / II} V^7 I

5. STUDY AND ANALYSIS

The following complete compositions are suggested for study and analysis.

Schumann—*Dichterliebe*:
        I. *Im wunderschönen Monat Mai.*

Bach—*Partita No. 5 in G major*:
        Tempo di Minuetta.

Mozart—*Piano Sonata, K. 331*: third movement.

Bach—Chorale #94: *Warum betrübst du dich, mein Herz.*

XIV / SECONDARY DOMINANTS

Required reading: Piston, Chapter 14.

The progression V–I may be duplicated on almost every degree of the major and minor scales by the use of secondary dominants, and the following example is a table of possibilities. The two triads missing from this table are VII in the major scale and II in the minor. They are diminished triads and for that reason cannot function as tonic chords.

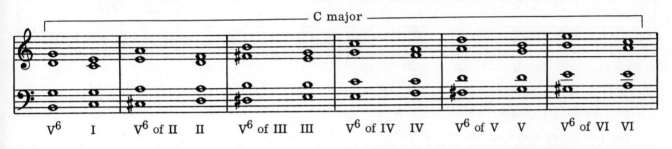

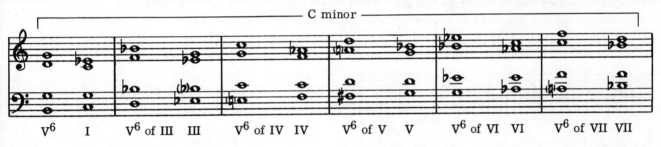

It must be observed that the chord to which a secondary dominant resolves is a chord in the key and requires no chromatic alteration.

THE APPROACH TO THE SECONDARY DOMINANT

A secondary dominant may be approached by a chord common to both the original key and to the key implied by the secondary dominant.

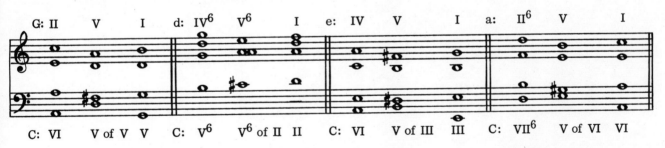

It may also be approached by a chord related only to the original key. In this kind of progression, it is important for the unaltered note to move to its chromatically altered form in the same voice. This is particularly true when the unaltered note appears in the soprano.

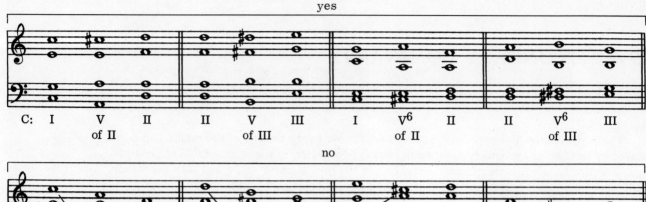

C: I V II II V III I V⁶ II II V⁶ III
   of II   of III   of II   of III

C: I V⁶ II II V⁶ III I V II II V III
   of II   of III   of II   of III

THE RESOLUTION OF THE SECONDARY DOMINANT

The secondary dominant, whether it be V, V^7, or VII, normally resolves to its tonic. The previous examples should illustrate this fact. The following two irregular resolutions, however, may be used if the chord of resolution belongs to the original key: V-VI, and V-IV^6.

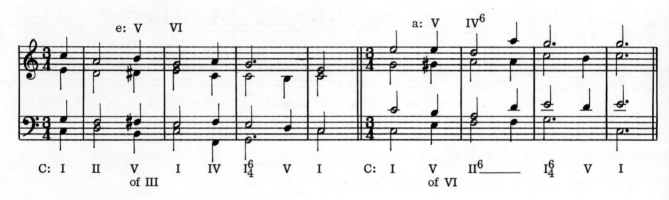

C: I II V I IV I⁶₄ V I   C: I V II⁶____ I⁶₄ V I
      of III   of VI

EXERCISES

1. Play or write the following chords in close position and resolve each of them to their tonic:

(a) V of II, V^6 of III, V of V, and V^6 of VI in G major;

(b) V^7 of II, V^6_5 of III, V^4_3 of V, and V^2 of VI in D major;

(c) V^6 of VII, V of VI, V^6 of IV, and V of III in B minor;

(d) V^2 of III, V^4_3 of IV, V^6_5 of VI, and V^7 of VII in F-sharp minor;

(e) V^6 of II, V of III, V^6 of V, and V of VI in A-flat major;

(f) V^2 of VI, V^4_3 of V, V^6_5 of III, and V^7 of II in B-flat major;

(g) V of VII, V^6 of VI, V of IV, and V^6 of III in C minor;

(h) V^7 of VII, V^6_5 of VI, V^4_3 of IV, and V^2 of III in D minor.

2. Harmonize each of the following melodic fragments in open position in two different ways: (1) without secondary dominants, and (2) with secondary dominants. The secondary dominants in this exercise are to be triads and not chords of the seventh.

(A)   (B)

C major

(C)   (D)

C major

(E)

Play the first harmonization of fragment (A) in G and D major;

Play the second harmonization of fragment (A) in D and A major;

Play the first harmonization of fragment (B) in F and B-flat major;

Play the second harmonization of fragment (B) in B-flat and E-flat major;

Play the first harmonization of fragment (C) in G and D major;

Play the second harmonization of fragment (C) in D and A major;

Play the first harmonization of fragment (D) in F and B-flat major;

Play the second harmonization of fragment (D) in B-flat and E-flat major;

Play the first harmonization of fragment (E) in G and D major;

Play the second harmonization of fragment (E) in D and A major.

3. Precede each of the following secondary dominants by an appropriate chord:

C major   G major   D major   A major

E major   B major   F♯ major   C♯ major

A minor   E minor   B minor   F♯ minor

C♯ minor   G♯ minor   E♭ minor   B♭ minor

4. Given the following harmonic skeletons, make four-part settings in open position:

(a) in C major (with E as the first note in the soprano)

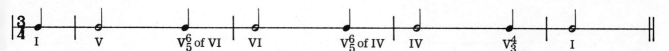

$$I \qquad V \qquad V^6_5 \text{ of VI} \quad VI \qquad V^6_5 \text{ of IV} \quad IV \qquad V^4_3 \qquad I$$

(b) in C major (with E as the first note in the soprano)

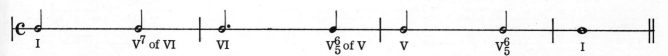

$$I \qquad V^7 \text{ of VI} \quad VI \qquad V^6_5 \text{ of V} \quad V \qquad V^6_5 \qquad I$$

(c) in C major (with C as the first note in the soprano)

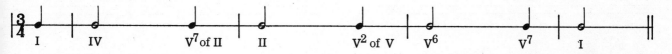

$$I \qquad IV \qquad V^7 \text{ of II} \quad II \qquad V^2 \text{ of V} \quad V^6 \qquad V^7 \qquad I$$

(d) in A minor (with C as the first note in the soprano)

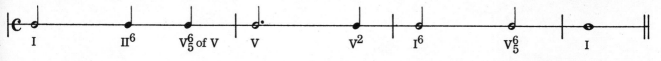

$$I \qquad II^6 \qquad V^6_5 \text{ of V} \quad V \qquad V^2 \qquad I^6 \qquad V^6_5 \qquad I$$

(e) in A minor (with C as the first note in the soprano)

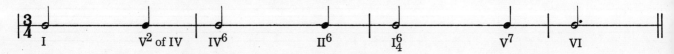

I   V² of IV   IV⁶   II⁶   I⁶₄   V⁷   VI

(f) in A minor (with C as the first note in the soprano)

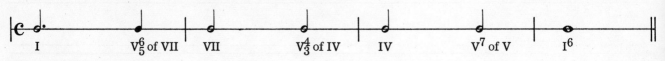

I   V⁶₅ of VII   VII   V⁴₃ of IV   IV   V⁷ of V   I⁶

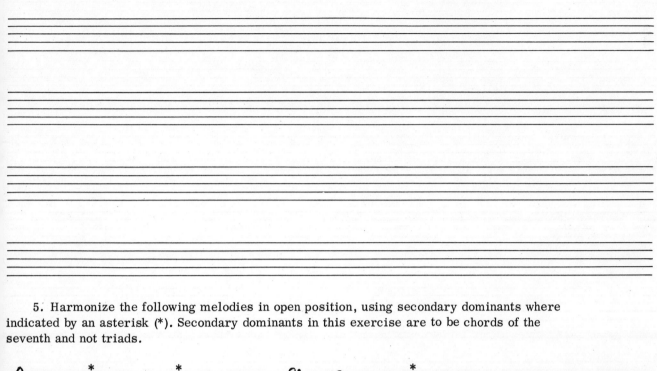

5. Harmonize the following melodies in open position, using secondary dominants where indicated by an asterisk (*). Secondary dominants in this exercise are to be chords of the seventh and not triads.

C major

A major

D major

A minor

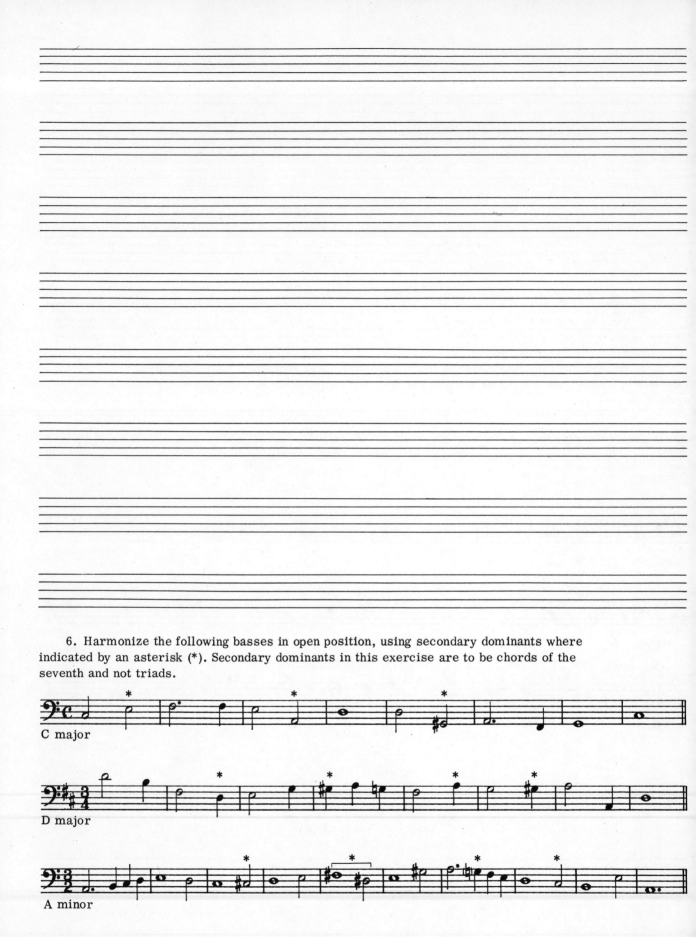

6. Harmonize the following basses in open position, using secondary dominants where indicated by an asterisk (*). Secondary dominants in this exercise are to be chords of the seventh and not triads.

7. STUDY AND ANALYSIS

The following excerpts are suggested for study and analysis.

Beethoven—*Piano Sonata No. 2, op. 2, No. 2*: third movement, measures 1 through 44.

Beethoven—*Piano Sonata No. 29, op. 106*: Second movement, measures 1 through 14.

Bach—*Fifteen Three-Part Inventions*: Invention 9, measures 26 through 35.

The following complete compositions are suggested for study and analysis.

Bach—Chorale #47: *Vater unser im Himmelreich*;
      Chorale #68: *Wenn wir in höchsten Nöten sein*.

Schumann—*Davidsbündlertänze*: X and XIV.

XV / THE SEQUENCE

Required reading: Piston, Chapter 19.

A harmonic sequence consists of a progression of two or more chords which is repeated on different degrees of the scale.

Pachelbel—*Gigue from Suite in D minor*

Although any harmonic progression can, theoretically at least, serve as the building block for a sequence, a close study of the music of the common-practice period reveals an important fact: the progressions used in sequence almost always involve root movement of a fifth, and specifically of a descending fifth. This fact should come as no surprise, for previous chapters have already emphasized the importance of this type of root movement from many different standpoints.

Even in those progressions involving more than two chords, root movement of a descending fifth is still clearly evident.

SEQUENCE PATTERNS

A harmonic progression of two chords based on root movement of a descending fifth can move in two different ways: (1) it can ascend or descend by step, or (2) it can ascend or descend by skip, usually by a skip of a third.

Harmonic progressions based on root movement of a third can also be used as the building block for a sequence, and examples of this kind can be found in the music of the common-practice period. At the same time, the fact must be recognized that all harmonic activities in this time are more or less dominated by the tonic-dominant principle and its implications in terms of root movement. Sequence is no exception, and the following excerpts can only suggest the variety possible within the limitation.

Schumann—*Aus den hebräischen Gesängen*

Denn sieh'! vom Kum - mer ward's ge - näh - ret, mit stum - mem Wa - chen trug____ es

Bach—*Partita No. 5: Gigue*

TONAL REPETITION OF THE PROGRESSION

When a progression moves in diatonic sequence, its appearance and "shape" remain the same, but the mode of the individual triads is changed.

As an example, the progression V^6-I, in C major, consists of two major triads; when this progression ascends to the next scale degree, it becomes VI^6-II, and then consists of two minor triads.

Such a sequence, therefore, involves tonal, not literal, repetition of the progression. Any attempt to repeat the progression in a literal manner will involve chromatic alteration and move the sequence out of the key.

SECONDARY DOMINANTS

Secondary dominants give chromatic color and dominant emphasis to a sequence but do not make it necessarily a modulating sequence. These chords normally resolve to their tonics, which are chords in the original key, and are only momentary departures from it.

When a sequence involves both secondary dominants and nonharmonic tones, it is important for these tones to belong to the key suggested by the secondary dominant.

PROGRESSIONS OF MORE THAN TWO CHORDS

The progression to be used in sequence is not limited as to size: it may consist of only two chords but may just as likely consist of several chords. When an extended progression is used in sequence, the original key is replaced by new, temporary keys. In this situation, it is important for all the notes within the progression to belong to the new key.

THE LEADING-TONE TRIAD

The leading-tone triad is a diminished triad in a major key and for this reason is seldom used in root position in a sequence apart from keyboard exercises. When a sequence using secondary dominants passes through the leading-tone triad, however, it may be used if it is chromatically altered to become a major triad.

THE SEQUENCE IN A MINOR KEY

A sequence in a minor key invariably shifts to its relative major rather than face the ambiguities of either the melodic or harmonic forms of the minor scale, particularly when it is ascending.

HARMONIC ANALYSIS

Harmonic analysis, which is simply a technique of explanation, always contains in itself several different approaches. For this reason, the student of harmony should not be discouraged to find that his analysis of a particular passage is capable of another interpretation.

It should already be clear that a modulating phrase can be analyzed in different ways; the sequence is also capable of different interpretations.

The student of harmony, as his musical experience increases, will find that there is no one simple solution to the problem of analysis. He will have to weigh and consider the two factors involved: (1) the relationship and importance of the chords to the original key, and (2) what is happening.

In the following example, a sequence has been analyzed in two different ways. In the first analysis the sequence is interpreted as a succession of chords, all related, in some manner, to the original key; the second analysis interprets the sequence as a series of interlocking progressions. Both analyses are "correct"; the second one, however, gives a more accurate description of what is happening.

EXERCISES

1. The following keyboard exercises bear little resemblance to the four-voiced vocal texture used for the written exercises in the entire workbook. The explanation for this lies in the fact that harmonic sequence is an integral element of instrumental music from the early Baroque to the late Romantic periods. These exercises are, as a consequence, instrumental rather than vocal in nature and, as a matter of fact, a distillation of the keyboard style of the late Baroque period.

The sequences can be played in two different ways: (1) diatonically, as written, and (2) with secondary dominants. The chromatic alterations required to make secondary dominants of certain chords or intervals in the sequences have not been specified and are left entirely up to the student.

Play sequence (A) in a diatonic manner in C, G, and D major;
Play sequence (A) with secondary dominants in G, D, and A major;

Play sequence (B) in a diatonic manner in C, F, and B-flat major;
Play sequence (B) with secondary dominants in F, B-flat and E-flat major;

Play sequence (C) in a diatonic manner in D, A, and E major;
Play sequence (C) with secondary dominants in A, E, and B major;

Play sequence (D) in a diatonic manner in F, B-flat, and E-flat major;
Play sequence (D) with secondary dominants in B-flat, E-flat, and A-flat major;

Play sequence (E) in a diatonic manner in C, G, and D major;
Play sequence (E) with secondary dominants in G, D, and A major;

Play sequence (F) in a diatonic manner in C, F, and B-flat major;
Play sequence (F) with secondary dominants in F, B-flat, and E-flat major.

2. The following two sequences involve secondary dominants and require no additional chromatic elaboration. The second sequence should ascend and descend in the manner specified by the first sequence in Exercise 1.

Play sequence (A) in C, G, and D major;

Play sequence (B) in C, F, and B-flat major.

3. Given the following harmonic skeletons, make four-part settings in open position:

(a) in C major (with E as the first note in the soprano)

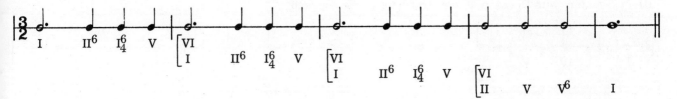

(b) In E-flat major (with E-flat as the first note in the soprano)

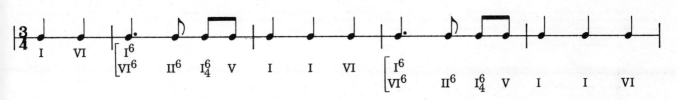

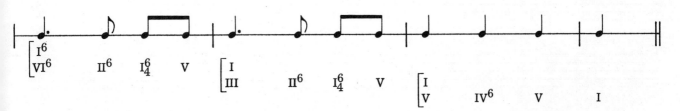

(c) In G major (with B as the first note in the soprano)

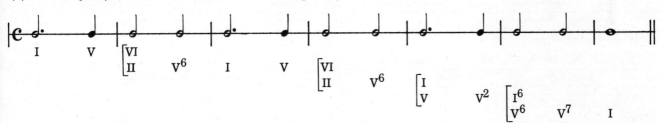

(d) in E major (with G-sharp as the first note in the soprano)

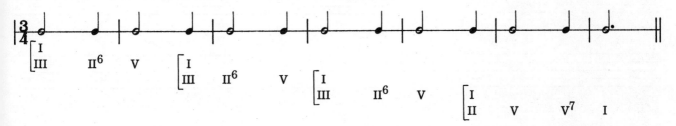

(e) in A-flat major (with E-flat as the first note in the soprano)

I   IV   I$^6_4$ V   VI
[VI
[I   IV   I$^6_4$ V   VI
      [VI
      [I   IV   I$^6_4$ V   VI
            [VI
            [II   V^7 I

(f) in B major (with D-sharp as the first note in the soprano)

I   IV   V
[VI
[I   IV   V
      [VI
      [I   IV   V
            [VI
            [II   V^6 I

4. Harmonize the following melodies in open position:

G major

Bb major

Db major

E major

5. Harmonize the following basses in open position:

A major

C major

Eb major

F# major

6. STUDY AND ANALYSIS

The following excerpts are suggested for study and analysis.

Bach—*The Well-Tempered Clavier*, Book I:
   Prelude II, measures 5 through 12;
   Prelude VI, measure 2 through the first quarter note of measure 6.

Bach—*Partita No. 1 in B-flat major*:
   Corrente, measure 5 through the first quarter note of measure 21;

   Partita No. 3 in A minor:
   Corrente, measure 5 through the first quarter note of measure 9;

   Partita No. 5 in G major:
   Corrente, measures 8 through 13, and measures 49 through 54.

Beethoven—*Piano Sonata No. 29, op. 106*: second movement, measure 1 through the first quarter note of measure 14;

   Piano Sonata No. 30, op. 109: first movement, measure 1 through the first quarter note of measure 4.

Chopin—*Etude op. 29, No. 9*: measure 1 through the first quarter note of measure 5.

XVI / THE DIMINISHED SEVENTH CHORD

Required reading: Piston, Chapters 16 and 22

PART ONE: DOMINANT HARMONY

The vocabulary of dominant harmony is further increased by the diminished seventh chord. This chord, the perfect embodiment of the harmonic minor scale—containing within itself the ascending form of the seventh degree and the descending form of the sixth degree—does not contain the crucial dominant degree of the scale. As a consequence, its inversions, from the standpoint of chord grammar, may be somewhat confusing. But it must be remembered that the dominant root is implied and not actually present in the chord, and that the inversions are calculated from the bass rather than from this root.

The Approach to the Diminished Seventh Chord

The diminished seventh chord, as V^0_9, can be approached by any triad in the key. If it is approached by V or VII, however, there is, in effect, no harmonic movement, since all of these chords are dominant in function.

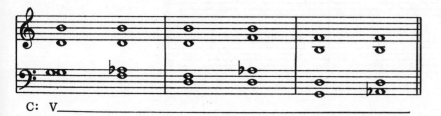

C: V_____

When the approach to the diminished seventh chord involves the chromatic alteration of a note, it should be handled in one of the following ways:

(1) the chromatic alteration should take place in one voice;

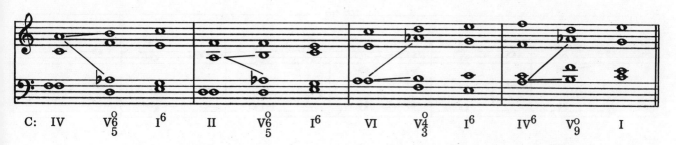

C: IV V^0_9 I II $V^0_{4\ 3}$ I^6 VI $V^0_{6\ 5}$ I^6 IV^6 V^0_2 I^6_4

(2) if the chromatic alteration involves two voices, the original note should, if at all possible, move stepwise.

C: IV $V^0_{6\ 5}$ I^6 II $V^0_{6\ 5}$ I^6 VI $V^0_{4\ 3}$ I^6 IV^6 V^0_9 I

169

The Resolution of the Diminished Seventh Chord

The required reading on this subject more than adequately describes the resolution of this chord in regard to the dissonant intervals which it contains. As a dominant chord, its resolution may also, however, be considered purely from the standpoint of the scale degrees involved and can be described by the following statements:

(1) 6 resolves to 5;

(2) 7 resolves to 8;

(3) 4 resolves to 3 but may resolve to 1 if it appears in the bass;

(4) 2 resolves to 3 or 5. It may also resolve to 1 if the resolution does not result in direct fifths.

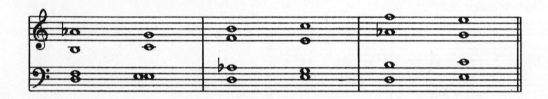

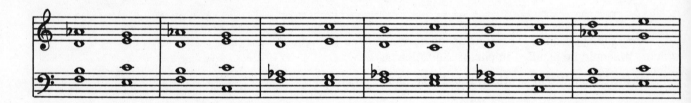

Although the diminished seventh chord in its dominant function normally resolves to I, it may also, in a minor key, resolve in the manner of a deceptive cadence to VI. It may also progress to IV and delay, in this way, the eventual resolution to I.

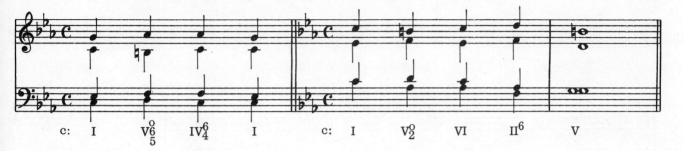

c: I   V$^0_6$$_5$ IV$^6_4$ I   c: I   V$^0_2$ VI   II^6 V

PART TWO: NON-DOMINANT HARMONY

The diminished seventh chord can be constructed on three different degrees of the scale: (1) as V$^0_9$, on the leading-tone degree with an implied dominant root; (2) as II^7 *altered*, on the chromatically raised supertonic degree; and (3) as VI^7 *altered*, on the chromatically raised submediant degree.

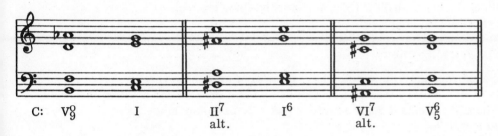

C: V$^0_9$ I   II^7 I^6 VI^7 V$^6_5$
                            alt.   alt.

Root Position and Inversion

From the standpoint of chord grammar, neither II^7 *altered* nor VI^7 *altered* presents any problem. The bottom notes of both chords in root position are their roots, and their inversions are calculated from these notes.

The Approach to II^7 altered and VI^7 altered

These two diminished seventh chords can be approached in a variety of ways, and no arbitrary set of rules could ever take precedence over a thoughtful consideration of the musical factors involved in this process.

From the standpoint of approach, some chords, however, are more effective than others. In the following example, II^7 *altered* is preceded by I, IV, and II; VI^7 *altered* is preceded by V, I, and VI.

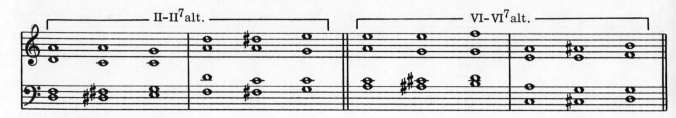

The Resolution of II⁷ altered and VI⁷ altered

The normal resolution of these chords is based upon an ascending stepwise resolution of their chromatically altered notes. The seventh of both chords ordinarily remains stationary; with II⁷ *altered*, the fifth of the chord ordinarily descends stepwise, and with VI⁷ *altered*, the fifth of the chord ordinarily ascends stepwise.

II⁷ altered and VI⁷ altered in a Minor Key

Both chords belong more appropriately in a major key. II⁷ *altered* may, however, be used in a minor key, usually in an auxiliary fashion and with complete disregard for notation. VI⁷ *altered*, containing as it does the mediant degree as it is found in the major mode, is much less frequently used in a minor key.

EXERCISES

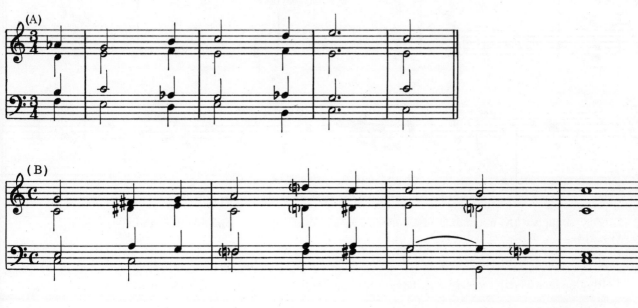

1. Play progression (A) in C, E-flat, G-flat, A, D-flat, E, G, and B-flat major;

   Play progression (B) in G-flat, A, D-flat, E, G, B-flat major, D, and F major;

   Play progression (C) in D-flat, E, G, B-flat major, D, F, A-flat, and B major.

etc.

etc.

2. Play sequence (A) ascending and descending an octave in C, B-flat, A-flat, and G-flat, major;

Play sequence (B) ascending and descending an octave in B, A, G, and F major;

Play sequence (C) ascending and descending an octave in E, D, C, and B-flat major;

Play sequence (D) ascending and descending an octave in E-flat, D-flat, B, and A major.

3. Given the following harmonic skeletons, make four-part settings in open position. *Note*: the melodic skip of an augmented second should, whenever possible, be avoided in the outer voices.

(a) in C major (with E as the first note in the soprano)

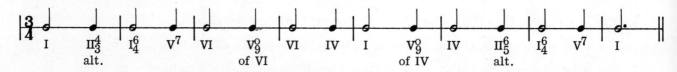

(b) in E-flat major (with B-flat as the first note in the soprano)

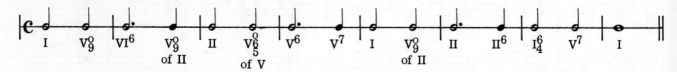

(c) in F-sharp major (with A-sharp as the first note in the soprano)

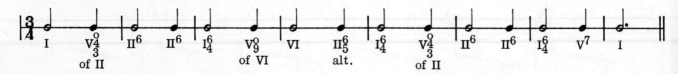

174

(d) in A major (with C-sharp as the first note in the soprano)

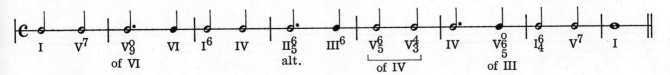

(e) in C-sharp minor (with C-sharp as the first note in the soprano)

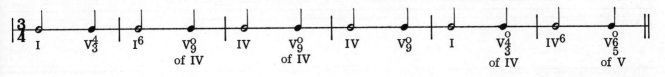

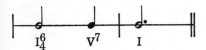

(f) in E minor (with B as the first note in the soprano)

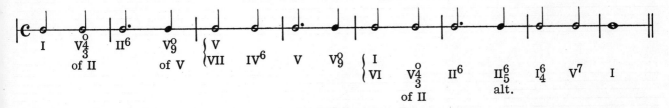

(g) in G major (with B as the first note in the soprano)

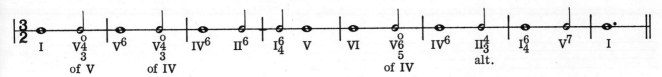

(h) in B-flat major (with D as the first note in the soprano)

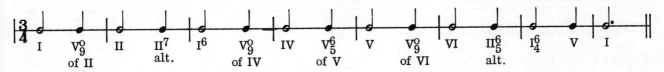

4. Harmonize the following melodies in open position, using diminished sevenths where indicated by an asterisk (*):

C major

G major

D major

A major

5. Harmonize the following basses in open position, using diminished sevenths where indicated by an asterisk (*):

E major

B major

F♯ major

C♯ minor

6. Any given diminished seventh chord can function in four different capacities: (1) as V; (2) as II^7 *altered*; (3) as VI^7 *altered*; and (4) as a secondary dominant in a number of different keys. This exercise and the one that follows it revolve about these four possibilities.

Each of the diminished seventh chords in this exercise must remain in its original notation throughout.

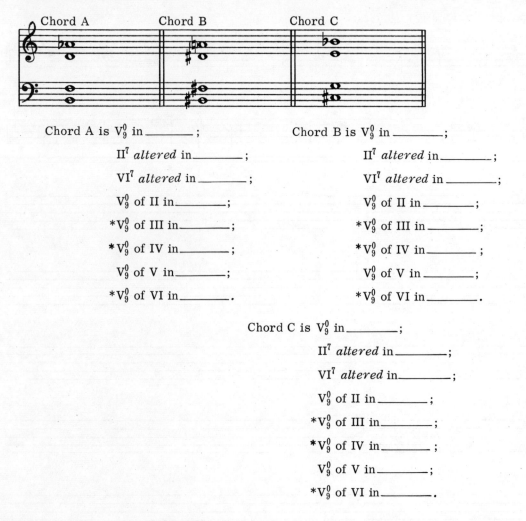

Chord A is V_9^0 in _____ ;   Chord B is V_9^0 in _____ ;

         II^7 *altered* in_____ ; II^7 *altered* in_____ ;

         VI^7 *altered* in _____ ; VI^7 *altered* in _____ ;

         V_9^0 of II in_____ ; V_9^0 of II in _____ ;

       *V_9^0 of III in_____ ;   *V_9^0 of III in _____ ;

       *V_9^0 of IV in_____ ;   *V_9^0 of IV in _____ ;

         V_9^0 of V in_____ ; V_9^0 of V in _____ ;

       *V_9^0 of VI in_____ .   *V_9^0 of VI in _____ .

                        Chord C is V_9^0 in_____ ;

                            II^7 *altered* in_____ ;

                          VI^7 *altered* in_____ ;

                            V_9^0 of II in _____ ;

                         *V_9^0 of III in_____ ;

                         *V_9^0 of IV in_____ ;

                            V_9^0 of V in_____ ;

                         *V_9^0 of VI in_____ .

*Two answers are possible in each instance because of the fact that the diminished seventh chord, in its dominant function, is used in both major and minor keys.

7. Resolve each of the diminished seventh chords in this exercise in a normal manner to the keys indicated and specify their correct notation in the different tonalities.

Resolve chord A as V_9^0 in C major;

as $V_{\frac{0}{5}}^6$ in A major;

as $V_{\frac{0}{3}}^4$ in G-flat major;

as V_2^0 in E-flat major;

as II^7 *altered* in A-flat major;

as II_5^6 *altered* in F major;

as II_3^4 *altered* in D major;

as II^2 *altered* in B major;

as VI^2 *altered* in E major;

as VI^7 *altered* in D-flat major;

as VI_5^6 *altered* in B-flat major;

as VI_3^4 *altered* in G major.

Resolve chord B as V_9^0 in C-sharp minor;

as $V_{\frac{0}{5}}^6$ in B-flat minor;

as $V_{\frac{0}{3}}^4$ in G minor;

as V_2^0 in E minor;

as II^7 *altered* in A major;

as II_5^6 *altered* in F-sharp major

as II_3^4 *altered* in E-flat major;

as II^2 *altered* in C major;

as VI^2 *altered* in F major;

as VI^7 *altered* in D major;

as VI_5^6 *altered* in B major;

as VI_3^4 *altered* in A-flat major.

Resolve chord C as V_9^0 in D major;

as $V_{\frac{0}{5}}^6$ in B major;

as $V_{\frac{0}{3}}^4$ in A-flat major;

as V_2^0 in F major;

Resolve chord C as II^7 *altered* in B-flat major;

as II^6_5 *altered* in G major;

as II^4_3 *altered* in E major;

as II^2 *altered* in D-flat major;

as VI^2 *altered* in F-sharp major;

as VI^7 *altered* in E-flat major;

as VI^6_5 *altered* in C major;

as VI^4_3 *altered* in A major.

8. STUDY AND ANALYSIS

The following excerpts are suggested for study and analysis.

Beethoven—*Piano Sonata No. 32, op. 111*: first movement, introduction only;

Beethoven—*Piano Sonata No. 30, op. 109*: first movement, measure 1 through the first eighth note of measure 14;

Piano Sonata No. 28, op. 101: first movement, measure 1 through the first quarter note of measure 25.

The following complete compositions are suggested for study and analysis.

Bach—Chorale #3: *Ach Gott, vom Himmel sieh' darein*;
Chorale #21: *Herzlich tut mich verlangen*;
Chorale #53: *Das neugeborne Kindelein*;
Chorale #59: *Herzliebster Jesu, was hast du*.

Bach—*French Suite No. 1 in D minor: Sarabande*;

English Suite No. 3 in G minor: Sarabande.

Schubert—*Schwanengesang:*
VIII. *Der Atlas*;
XI. *Die Stadt*.

Schumann—*Dichterliebe:*
VI. *Im Rhein, im heiligen Strome*;
V. *Ich will mein Seele tauchen*.

XVII / THE INCOMPLETE MAJOR NINTH AND THE COMPLETE DOMINANT NINTH

Required reading: Piston, Chapters 17 and 18.

PART ONE: THE INCOMPLETE MAJOR NINTH

The diminished seventh, as V_9^0, and the incomplete major ninth are similar in two respects: they are constructed from the same scale degrees, and they both, as their grammar indicates, function as dominant chords.

Their differences are, however, more striking. Most important of all is the fact that the diminished seventh can be used in either a major or a minor key, while the incomplete major ninth can function well only in a major key. Next in importance is the fact that the diminished seventh, being made up of equidistant intervals, sounds the same whether it is in root position or in inversion and is, for this reason, a flexible pivot chord for modulation; the incomplete major ninth, being made up of thirds of different kinds, does not have this flexibility.

Root Position and Inversion

From the standpoint of chord grammar, the inversions of the incomplete major ninth are calculated in the same manner as the inversions of the diminished seventh. A subtle distinction in regard to scoring must, however, be noted: the incomplete major ninth is most effective when the seventh of the chord appears in the soprano or at least above the root.

The Approach to the Incomplete Major Ninth

The incomplete major ninth can be approached in a variety of ways, but is most easily approached by I, II, or IV. Again, if it is approached by either V or VII, there is, in effect, no harmonic movement, since all of these chords are dominant in function.

There are no chromatic alterations involved in the approach to this chord; the only problems to be considered are the normal ones of voice-leading.

The Resolution of the Incomplete Major Ninth

The incomplete major ninth normally resolves to the tonic and its resolution, considered from the standpoint of voice-leading, is similar to the normal resolution of the diminished seventh.

It may also, and particularly in a sequential passage, resolve to III, and in this situation is more properly described as VII^7.

If it resolves to VI, the progression strongly suggests the relative minor and can easily be interpreted as II^7-I.

A last possibility is the progression to IV, which delays the inevitable resolution to I.

C: V_9^0 I   C: VII^7 III   a: II_5^6 I   C: V_9^0 IV_4^6 I

The Incomplete Major Ninth as a Pivot Chord

The incomplete major ninth can function in three different capacities: (1) as V_9^0 in a major key; (2) as II^7 in its related minor key; and (3) as a secondary dominant in a number of major keys. Its possibilities as a pivot chord will be exploited in Exercise 6 at the end of this chapter.

PART TWO: THE COMPLETE DOMINANT NINTH

Root Position and Inversion

The complete dominant ninth is most frequently used in root position and with the fifth of the chord omitted. Some inversions are possible; in one of them the third rather than the fifth of the chord is omitted. Regardless of the position of the chord and what chord tone is omitted, however, the ninth almost always appears in the soprano with the root of the chord appearing in either the tenor or the bass. Example 453 in the required reading for this chapter, as well as the following excerpt, should substantiate this fact.

Chopin—*Mazurka, op. 63, No. 2*

It is only in the late nineteenth and twentieth centuries that composers rearranged this chord to stress its dissonant elements.

Könnt' ich, Herr, für dich sie tra - gen, da es To - des - wun - den sind.

The Approach to and Resolution of the Complete Dominant Ninth

The complete dominant ninth is most easily approached by I, II, or IV in the major mode and by I or IV in the minor mode.

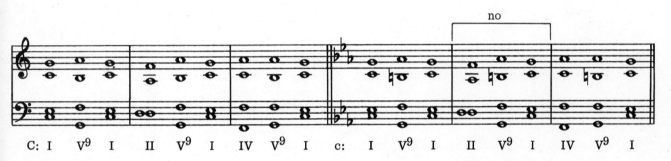

C: I V^9 I   II V^9 I   IV V^9 I   c: I V^9 I   II V^9 I   IV V^9 I

The normal resolution of the chord to the tonic, considered from the standpoint of the scale degrees involved, can be described by the following statements:

(1) 6 resolves to 5;

(2) 4 resolves to 3;

(3) 7 resolves to 8;

(4) 5 resolves to 1, or remains stationary.

Although the complete dominant ninth normally resolves to the tonic, it may, in root position, resolve in the manner of a deceptive cadence to VI. It may also progress to IV.

188

EXERCISES

1. Play progression (A) in C, F, B-flat, E-flat, and A-flat major;

   Play progression (B) in C, G, D, A, and E major;

   Play progression (C) in G, C, F, B-flat, and E-flat major;

   Play progression (D) in G, D, A, E, and B major;

   Play progression (E) in C, G, D, A, and E minor.

2.

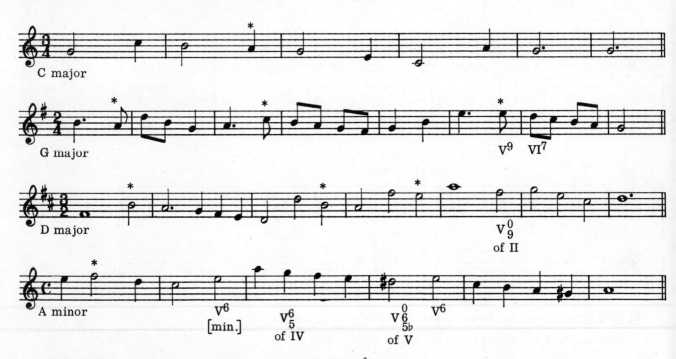

Play sequence (A) ascending and descending an octave in C, G, D, and A major;

Play sequence (B) ascending and descending an octave in C, F, B-flat, and E-flat major.

Note: the mode of the dominant ninth is determined by the mode of the chord to which it resolves.

3. Harmonize the following melodies in open position, using incomplete major ninths or complete dominant ninths where specified by an asterisk (*):

Note: When a diminished seventh chord is used as V_9^0 in a major key, the chord symbol should indicate the chromatic alteration ($V_{9\flat}^0$, $V_{\substack{6 \\ 5\flat}}^0$, as examples).

190

4. Harmonize the following basses in open position, using incomplete major ninths or complete dominant ninths where specified by an asterisk (*):

5. Given the following harmonic skeletons, make four-part settings in open position:

(a) in F major (with A as the first note in the soprano)

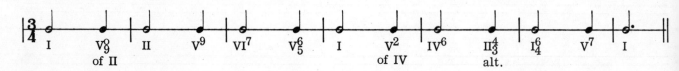

(b) in B-flat major (with D as the first note in the soprano)

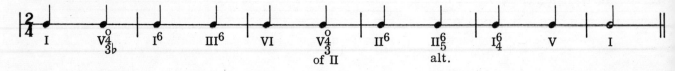

(c) in E-flat major (with E-flat as the first note in the soprano)

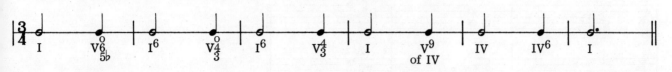

(d) in A-flat major (with F as the first note in the soprano)

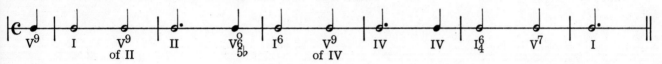

6. Complete the following statements orally or in writing.

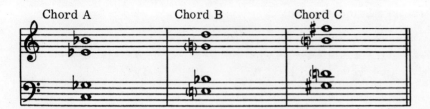

Chord A   Chord B   Chord C

Chord A is V_9^0 in _____.   Chord B is V_9^0 in _____.
          II^7 in _____. II^7 in _____.
          V_9^0 of III in _____. V_9^0 of III in _____.
          V_9^0 of IV in _____. V_9^0 of IV in _____.
          V_9^0 of V in _____. V_9^0 of V in _____.
          V_9^0 of VI in _____. V_9^0 of VI in _____.

                    Chord C is V_9^0 in _____.
                              II^7 in _____.
                              V_9^0 of III in _____.
                              V_9^0 of IV in _____.
                              V_9^0 of V in _____.
                              V_9^0 of VI in _____.

7. Complete the following statements orally or in writing.

Note: the mode of the complete dominant ninth is determined by the mode of the key to which it belongs, even though the minor dominant ninth is sometimes used in a major key.

V^9 of IV in C major is V^9 of III in _____ .

V^9 of IV in D major is V^9 of VI in _____ .

V^9 of IV in E major is V^9 of V in _____ .

V^9 of IV in G minor is V^9 of II in _____ .

V^9 of IV in A minor is V^9 of III in _____ .

V^9 of IV in B minor is V^9 of VI in _____ .

V^9 of II in D major is V^9 of VI in _____ .

V^9 of II in E major is V^9 of III in _____ .

V^9 of II in F-sharp major is V^9 of IV in _____ .

V^9 of III in A minor is V^9 of IV in _____ .

V^9 of III in B minor is V^9 of VI in _____ .

V^9 of III in C-sharp minor is V^9 of V in _____ .

V^9 of III in E major is V^9 of VI in _____.

V^9 of III in G-flat major is V^9 of IV in _____.

V^9 of III in A-flat major is V^9 of II in _____.

8. STUDY AND ANALYSIS

The following excerpt is suggested for study and analysis.

Schubert—*Piano Sonata in B-flat major (1828)*: second movement, measures 1 through 42.

The following complete compositions are suggested for study and analysis.

Schumann—*Liederkreis, op. 39*:
　　　　　　　X. *Zwielicht*, measure 24 to the end;
　　　　　　　V. *Mondnacht*, measures 1 through 13;
　　　　　　　XII. *Frühlingsnacht*, measures 1 through 10.

XVIII / NONDOMINANT HARMONY: SEVENTH, NINTH, ELEVENTH, AND THIRTEENTH CHORDS

Required reading: Piston, Chapters 20 and 21.

PART ONE: NONDOMINANT SEVENTH CHORDS

The vocabulary of nondominant harmony is enlarged by the use of seventh chords. These chords are constructed upon every degree of both the major and minor scales. The only degree not involved is the fifth degree, since a seventh chord constructed upon this degree is a dominant chord.

The following example is a compilation of commonly used nondominant sevenths in both the major and minor keys. In a major key, there are six different nondominant sevenths; in a minor key, there are eleven different nondominant sevenths. The greater number of possibilities in a minor key rests upon the fact that the sixth and seventh degrees of this scale may be either raised or lowered, depending upon the direction of the melody or of one of the voices. At the same time, some of these possibilities are preferred to others: nondominant sevenths which contain the descending form of the sixth or seventh degrees are used more frequently and with more ease than the nondominant sevenths which contain the ascending form of the sixth or seventh degrees.

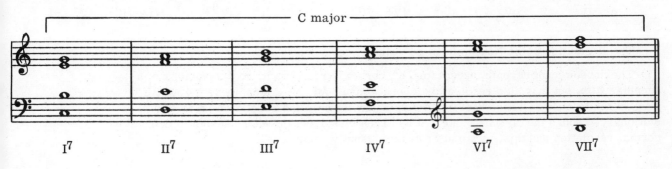

Root Position and Inversion

The nondominant seventh, like the dominant seventh, may be used in root position or in inversion, and the grammar of its inversions is identical with the grammar of the dominant seventh. If melodic considerations make it advisable to omit one of the chord tones, it is invariably the fifth of the chord that is omitted, with a consequent doubling of the root of the chord.

C: II⁷ _____ II⁶₅ _____ II⁴₃ _____ II² _____

The Approach to the Nondominant Seventh

The nondominant seventh may be approached by any chord in the key. In a minor key, care must be taken to avoid the melodic skip of an augmented second and to approach, as well as to quit, the nondominant seventh in a way that will emphasize the melodic rather than the harmonic form of the scale.

c: IV⁷ V V⁶₅ I I⁶ IV² VII⁶ I I⁷ II² V⁶₅ I VI⁷ II⁶ V⁷ I

The Resolution of the Nondominant Seventh

The nondominant seventh, except for IV⁷, normally resolves by root movement of a descending fifth, but may also resolve to a chord whose root lies a step above its own. If it progresses to a chord whose root lies a step below its own, the resolution is, in effect, stationary. Though the dissonant interval has been dissolved, the chord seems to demand its normal resolution and this, as a matter of fact, usually occurs.

C: II⁷ V I   II⁷ III VI V I   II⁷ I⁶ II⁶ I⁶₄ V I

The Nondominant Seventh as a Pivot Chord

The nondominant seventh is most effective as a pivot chord; the following example, limited to one particular kind, should illustrate some of its potentiality.

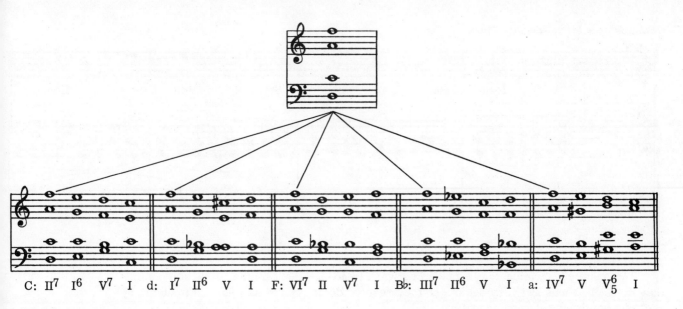

C: II⁷ I⁶ V⁷ I   d: I⁷ II⁶ V I   F: VI⁷ II V⁷ I   B♭: III⁷ II⁶ V I   a: IV⁷ V V⁶₅ I

The Sequential Chain of Nondominant Sevenths

The nondominant seventh, in its normal resolution, may resolve to a seventh rather than to a triad, and this progression has often been used in sequence.

In this progression, the third of the first chord remains stationary and becomes the seventh of the second chord.

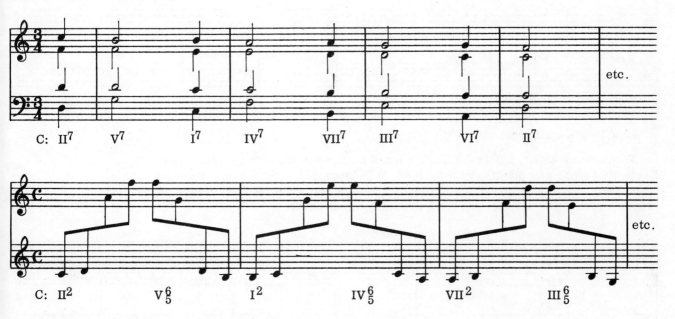

C: II⁷   V⁷   I⁷   IV⁷   VII⁷   III⁷   VI⁷   II⁷   etc.

C: II²   V⁶₅   I²   IV⁶₅   VII²   III⁶₅   etc.

PART TWO: THE NONDOMINANT NINTH

The complete dominant ninth is often not a distinct chord but rather a dominant seventh, elaborated by an appoggiatura or a suspension.

Schumann—*Mein schöner Stern*!

The same observation can be made in regard to nondominant ninths. Very seldom are they distinct chords and very seldom do they resolve directly, and in a normal manner, by root movement of a descending fifth.

Nondominant ninths, in the music of the common-practice period, are limited, to a great extent, to the following possibilities: I, II, IV, and VI in a major key, and I, III, IV, and VI in a minor key.

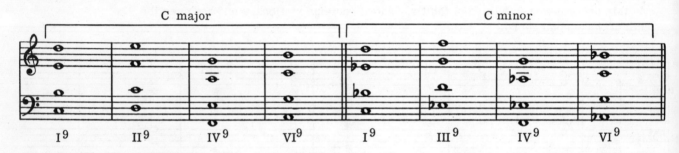

Root Position and Inversion

Nondominant ninths, within the framework of a four-part harmonic texture, function effectively only in root position with the ninth in the soprano. The complete dominant ninth can be used in inversion to a limited extent; when the same spacings are used for nondominant ninths, however, the nature of the chord is completely dissipated.

The Approach to the Nondominant Ninth

The problem of the approach to the nondominant ninth is a problem of counterpoint. The ninth in the outer voices should be approached by oblique or contrary motion.

C: VI   II⁹   IV   II⁹   III   II⁹   II   II⁹

The Resolution of the Nondominant Ninth

The problem of the resolution of the nondominant ninth is, again, a problem of counterpoint, and is best solved by having the ninth and seventh of the chord descend as parallel thirds while the bass skips up a fourth or down a fifth, remains stationary, or ascends stepwise.

C major   C minor

C: II⁹   V   II⁹   V⁷   II⁹   VII⁶   II⁹   III⁷   c: I⁹   IV   I⁹   IV⁷   I⁹   VI⁶   I⁹   II⁷

PART THREE: ELEVENTH AND THIRTEENTH CHORDS

The required reading in regard to these chords clearly illustrates the fact that they can, almost always, be interpreted not as elevenths or thirteenths but as simpler chords involving either a pedal or nonharmonic tones.

The following example, though it falls outside the limits of the common-practice period, is a case in point. It is without question I^{11} in E minor, and all of the chord tones are present. At the same time, the chordal structure of thirds is nowhere evident: indeed, it is seconds and fourths, rather than thirds, that dominate the texture.

Ravel—*Soupir*

- tom - ne jon - ché   de ta - ches de rous-seur

It is important to understand the fact that eleventh and thirteenth chords are, to a great extent, theoretical abstractions, that they are practically never found in their complete forms, that they can almost always be interpreted as simpler chords, and that they appeared in a period in music history when the traditional structure of chords was being slowly but inevitably destroyed by linear considerations.

The following eleventh chords, all in root position, are, however, possible within the framework of a four-part harmonic texture. The eleventh and ninth of the chord ordinarily resolve stepwise downward; the bass either remains stationary, or skips up a fourth or down a fifth.

The question of harmonic analysis and interpretation inevitably arises: is the eleventh chord a distinct chord or some kind of dominant over a tonic pedal?

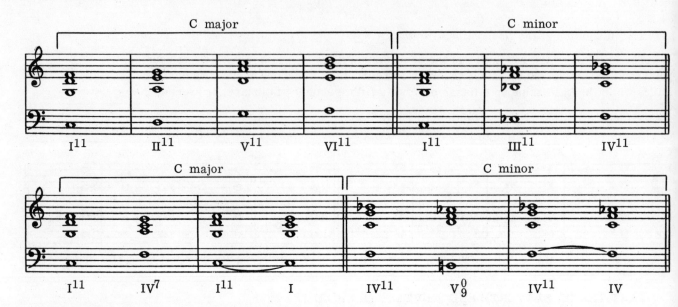

In regard to the thirteenth chord, the problem of reducing a seven-note chord into a four-part harmonic texture is almost an absurdity. Two thirteenth chords, one dominant and the other nondominant, are, however, employed within this framework, and they are I^{13} and V^{13}. There is, again, a question of harmonic analysis: the first chord can be considered V_9^0 over a tonic pedal; the second chord can be considered V^7 with a "frozen" appoggiatura.

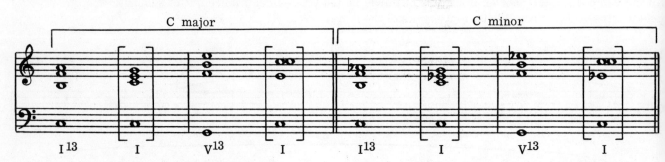

EXERCISES

1. Play progression (A) in C, G, and D major;

   Play progression (B) in D, A, and E major;

   Play progression (C) in C, F, and B-flat minor;

   Play progression (D) in D, G, and C minor;

   Play progression (E) in E, B, and F-sharp major.

2. Play sequence (A) in C, E-flat, F-sharp, and A major;

   Play sequence (B) in C, E, G, and B-flat major;

   Play sequence (C) in C, F, A-flat, and B major;

   Play sequence (D) in C, D, F, and A-flat major.

3. Given the following harmonic skeletons, make four-part settings in open position:

(a) in G major (with B as the first note in the soprano)

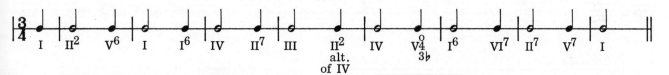

I   II²   V⁶   I   I⁶   IV   II⁷   III   II² alt. of IV   IV   V$^{0\frac{4}{3}\flat}$ I⁶   VI⁷   II⁷   V⁷   I

(b) in D major (with A as the first note in the soprano)

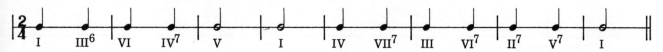

I   III⁶   VI   IV⁷   V   I   IV   VII⁷   III   VI⁷   II⁷   V⁷   I

(c) in A major (with E as the first note in the soprano)

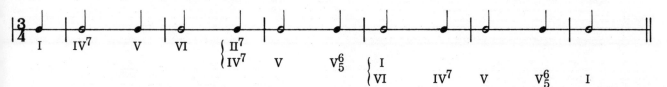

I   IV⁷   V   VI   { II⁷ / IV⁷ }   V   V$_5^6$ { I / VI }   IV⁷   V   V$_5^6$ I

(d) in E major (with B as the first note in the soprano)

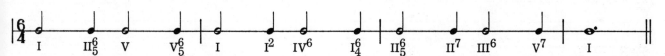

I   II$_5^6$ V   V$_5^6$ I   I²   IV⁶   I$_4^6$ II$_5^6$ II⁷   III⁶   V⁷   I

(e) in E minor (with B as the first note in the soprano)

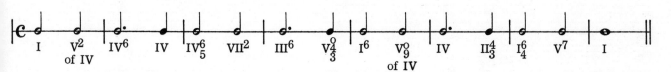

I   V² of IV   IV⁶   IV   IV$_5^6$ VII²   III⁶   V$^{0\frac{4}{3}}$ I⁶   V$_9^0$ of IV   IV   II$_3^4$ I$_4^6$ V⁷   I

(f) in B minor (with D as the first note in the soprano)

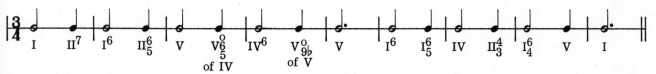

I   II⁷   I⁶   II$_5^6$ V   V$_5^{06}$ of IV   IV⁶   V$_{9\flat}^0$ of V   V   I⁶   I$_5^6$ IV   II$_3^4$ I$_4^6$ V   I

(g) in F-sharp minor (with A as the first note in the soprano)

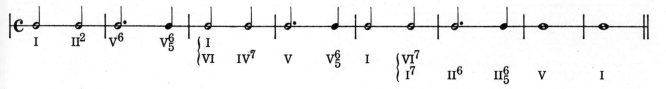

I   II²   V⁶   V$_5^6$ { I / VI }   IV⁷   V   V$_5^6$ I   { VI⁷ / I⁷ }   II⁶   II$_5^6$ V   I

(h) in C-sharp minor (with G-sharp as the first note in the soprano)

$\begin{array}{c}3\\4\end{array}$

I   V^2 of IV $\begin{cases} \text{IV}^6 \\ \text{VI}^6 \end{cases}$ I^7 II^6 V$\begin{smallmatrix}\circ\\4\\3\flat\end{smallmatrix}$ I^6 $\begin{cases} \text{VI} \\ \text{IV} \end{cases}$ V$\begin{smallmatrix}\circ\\9\flat\end{smallmatrix}$ of V   V   V^7 I

4. STUDY AND ANALYSIS

The following complete compositions are suggested for study and analysis.

Bach—*English Suite No. 3 in G minor: Sarabande*;

      Partita No. 6 in E minor: Sarabande.

Schumann—*Frauenliebe und -leben, op. 42:*
      2. *Er, der Herrlichste;*
      6. *Süsser Freund.*

Brahms—*Intermezzo, op. 119, No. 1.*

XIX / CHROMATIC CHORDS

Required reading: Piston, Chapter 23, 24, and 25

PART ONE: THE NEAPOLITAN SIXTH

Root Position and Inversion

The Neapolitan sixth is the first inversion of a major triad constructed on the lowered supertonic degree of the scale. It is normally used in first inversion, although examples of this chord in root position can be found in the music of the common-practice period.

The most common doubling is that of the third of the triad which is a tonal degree of the scale, and this doubling emphasizes the subdominant quality of the chord.

The Approach to the Neapolitan Sixth in a Minor Key

The Neapolitan sixth in a minor key is effectively approached by I, IV, or VI. In the progression I-N^6, care must be taken to avoid parallel fifths.

C minor

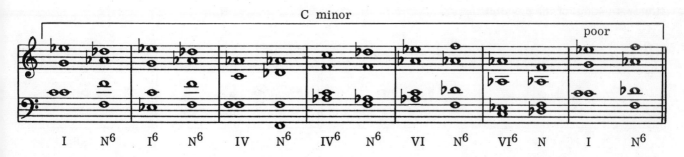

$I \quad N^6 \quad I^6 \quad N^6 \quad IV \quad N^6 \quad IV^6 \quad N^6 \quad VI \quad N^6 \quad VI^6 \quad N \quad I \quad N^6$

The Approach to the Neapolitan Sixth in a Major Key

The Neapolitan sixth in a major key is effectively approached by I, or by IV or VI if they are "shifted" in mode. In the progression I-N^6, care must be taken not only to avoid parallel fifths but also to avoid the melodic skip of an augmented second, particularly in the soprano.

C major

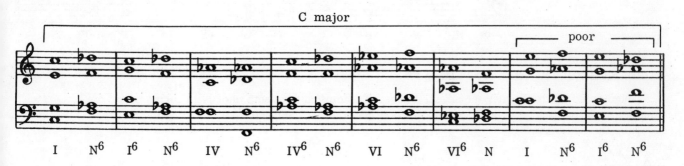

$I \quad N^6 \quad I^6 \quad N^6 \quad IV \quad N^6 \quad IV^6 \quad N^6 \quad VI \quad N^6 \quad VI^6 \quad N \quad I \quad N^6 \quad I^6 \quad N^6$

The Cadential Use of the Neapolitan Sixth

Each of the following seven cadences contains a Neapolitan sixth and it is important to observe that the root of the chord moves in the direction of its chromatic alteration, down either to the leading-tone or tonic degrees.

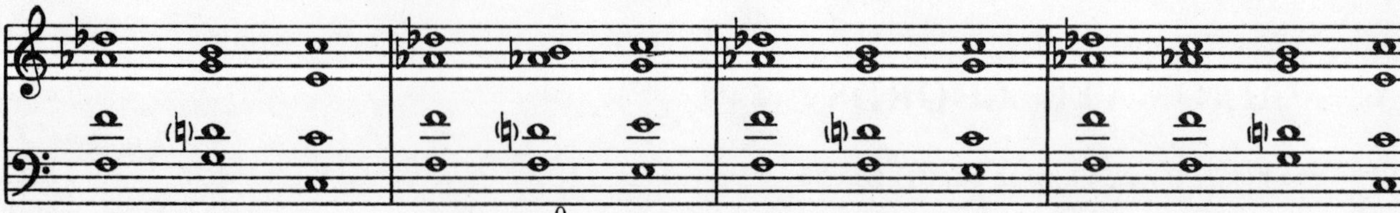

C: N^6 V I N^6 $V^{0}_{4\,3\flat}$ I^6 N^6 V^2 I^6 N^6 IV V I

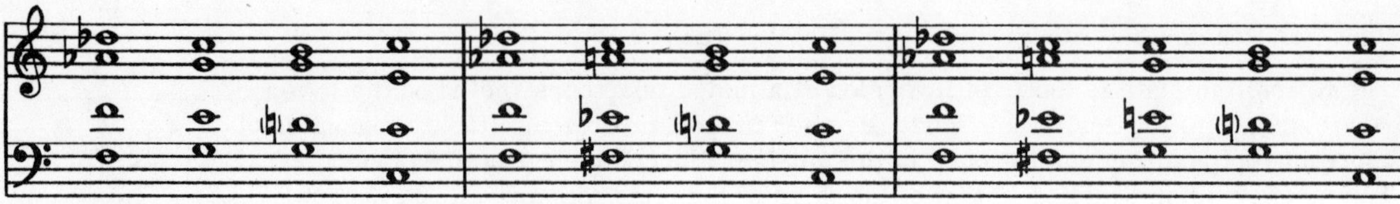

N^6 I^6_4 V I N^6 $V^{0}_{9\flat}$ of V V I N^6 $V^{0}_{9\flat}$ of V I^6_4 V I

The Neapolitan Sixth as a Pivot Chord

The Neapolitan sixth, being a major triad, is capable of many different interpretations and can, therefore, work extremely well as a pivot chord. The following example should illustrate some of the possibilities.

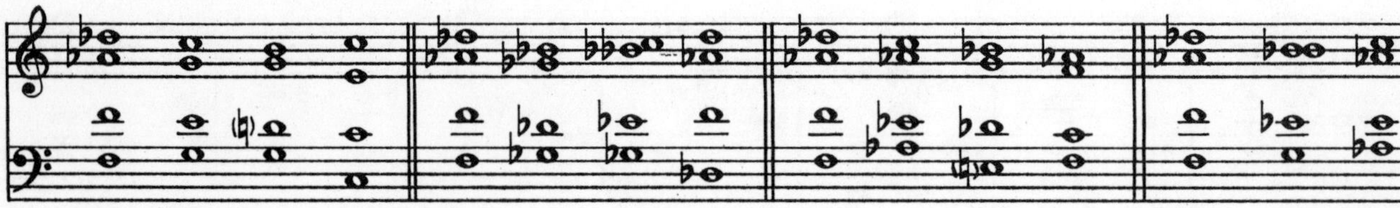

C: N^6 I^6_4 V I D♭: I^6 IV $V^{0}_{4\,3\flat}$ I f: VI^6 III V^{0}_{9} I A♭: IV^6 V^6 I

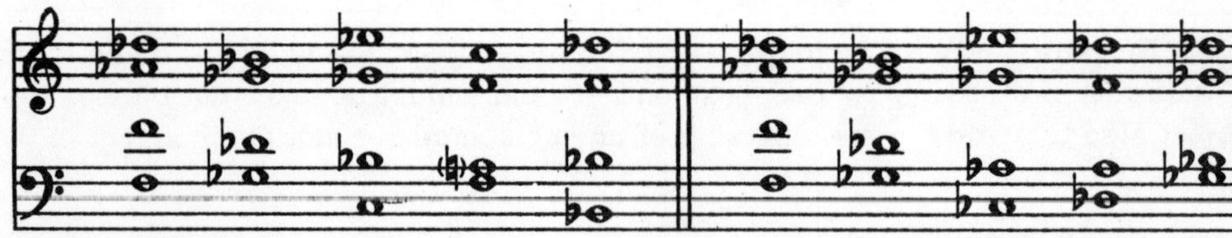

b♭: III^6 VI II^7 V I G♭: V^6 I II^6_5 V I

PART TWO: THE AUGMENTED SIXTH

Augmented sixth chords, though they resemble dominant seventh chords in terms of sound, are actually nondominant chords that are "reaching," through their chromatic alteration, for the dominant.

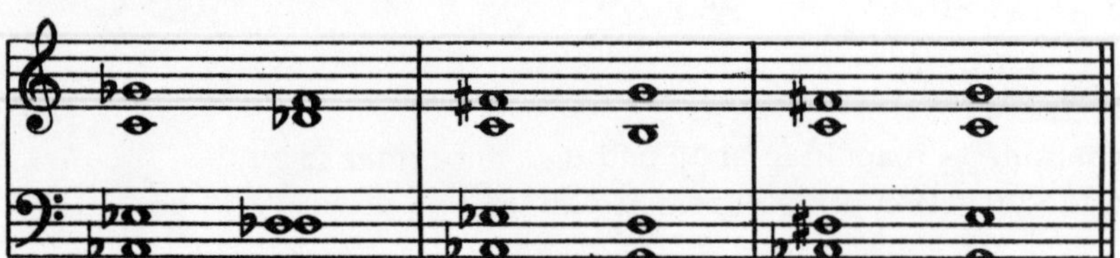

D♭: V^7 I C: $IV^{6\sharp}_{5}$ V $II^{6\sharp}_{4\sharp}$ V

Chord Grammar

The four kinds of augmented sixth chords have three tones in common; it is the fourth tone and the manner of its motion that determines how the chord will be written and what it will be called.

Root Position and Inversion

Augmented sixth chords are most frequently used with the augmented sixth interval in the outer voices, but may also be used in root position and in other inversion forms.

The Approach to and Resolution of the Augmented Sixth

The augmented sixth is most effectively approached by I, IV, V, or VI, and resolves to either a tonic or dominant chord. The chord of resolution determines how the augmented sixth will be written and what it will be called. In the progression I-II$^{6\#}_{4\ 3}$, care must be taken to avoid the melodic skip of an augmented second in the soprano. The parallel fifths that usually occur in the progression IV$^{6\#}_{5\ 3}$-V are permissible if they do not occur in the outer voices.

C minor

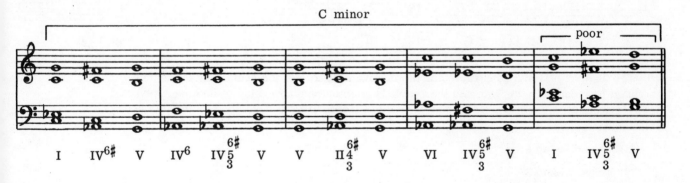

211

C major

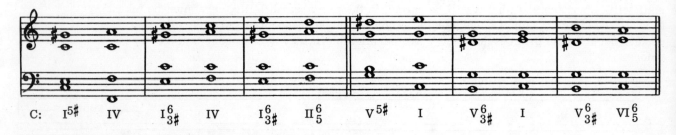

I   IV⁶♯   V   IV⁶   IV⁵♯₃   V   V   II⁴₃♯   V   VI   IV⁵♯₃   V   VI   II⁴₃♯   V   I   II⁴₃♯   I⁶₄

The Augmented Sixth as a Pivot Chord

The four augmented sixth chords may function as pivot chords by resolving enharmonically as a dominant seventh chord. The following example reveals some of the possibilities that exist with one of the augmented sixth chords.

C: IV⁶♯₅₃   V   D♭: V⁷   VI   V⁷   I   V⁷   IV⁶

PART THREE: DIMINISHED AND AUGMENTED TRIADS

Augmented triads may be constructed, in a major key, on the tonic, subdominant, and dominant degrees of the scale, but the two most frequently used are those constructed on the tonic and dominant degrees. Their resolution normally involves a stepwise ascent of the third and fifth of the chord. The resolutions possible within this limitation are illustrated in the following example.

C: I⁵♯   IV   I⁶₃♯   IV   I⁶₃♯   II⁶₅   V⁵♯   I   V⁶₃♯   I   V⁶₃♯   VI⁶₅

The augmented triad constructed on the dominant degree of the scale may be further extended by means of a seventh and the result is another, and new, kind of dominant seventh: V⁷₅♯. Its resolution, from the standpoint of scale degrees, may be described by the following statements:

(1) 7 resolves to 8;

(2) 4 resolves to 3;

(3) 2, in its chromatically raised from, resolves to 3.

(4) 5 moves to 1, or remains stationary.

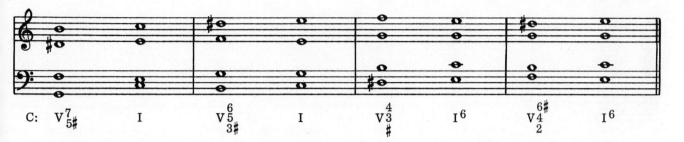

$$\text{C:} \quad V^7_{5\sharp} \qquad \text{I} \qquad V^6_{5\atop 3\sharp} \qquad \text{I} \qquad V^4_{3\atop \sharp} \qquad \text{I}^6 \qquad V^{6\sharp}_{4\atop 2} \qquad \text{I}^6$$

The fifth of the dominant seventh chord is often chromatically lowered, and the result is another, and new, kind of dominant seventh: $V^7_{5\flat}$. In terms of sound it is identical with $II^{6\sharp}_{4\atop 3}$. The difference lies in its placement in the scale.

Its resolution, from the standpoint of scale degrees, may be described by the following statements:

(1) 7 resolves to 8;

(2) 4 resolves to 3;

(3) 2, in its chromatically lowered form, resolves to 1.

(4) 5 moves to 1, or remains stationary.

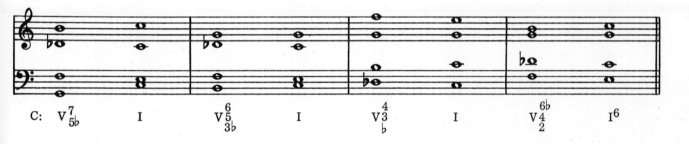

$$\text{C:} \quad V^7_{5\flat} \qquad \text{I} \qquad V^6_{5\atop 3\flat} \qquad \text{I} \qquad V^4_{3\atop \flat} \qquad \text{I} \qquad V^{6\flat}_{4\atop 2} \qquad \text{I}^6$$

EXERCISES

1. Play progression (A) in C, F, and B-flat minor;

   Play progression (B) in C, G, and D minor;

   Play progression (C) in C, E, and A-flat major;

   Play progression (D) in C, G-sharp, and E minor;

   Play progression (E) in C, G, and D major;

   Play progression (F) in C, F, and B-flat major;

   Play progression (G) in C, A, and F-sharp minor;

   Play progression (H) in C, A, and F-sharp major.

(C)

Play sequence (A) in C, G, and D major, ascending and descending an octave;

Play sequence (B) in C, F, and B-flat major, ascending and descending an octave;

Play sequence (C) in C, E, and A-flat major, ascending and descending an octave.

3. Given the following harmonic skeletons, make four-part settings in open position:

(a) in C major (with G as the first note in the soprano)

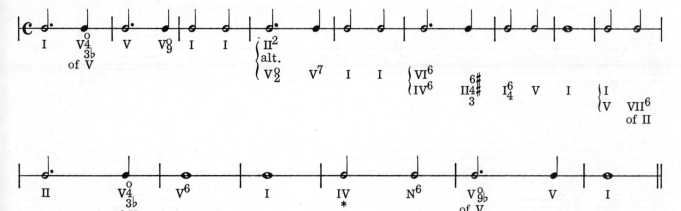

(b) in G major (with D as the first note in the soprano)

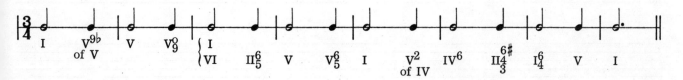

(c) in D minor (with F as the first note in the soprano)

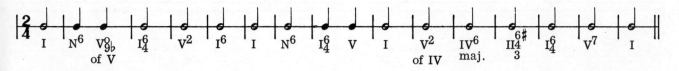

*constituted as it would be in the minor mode.

(d) in A major (with C-sharp as the first note in the soprano)

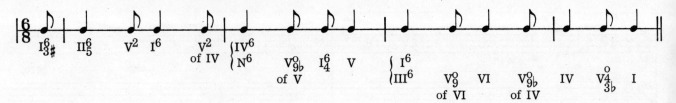

$I_{3\#}^{6}$ II_{5}^{6} V^2 I^6 V^2 of IV $\begin{cases} IV^6 \\ N^6 \end{cases}$ $V_{9\flat}^{o}$ of V I_{4}^{6} V $\begin{cases} I^6 \\ III^6 \end{cases}$ V_{9}^{o} of VI   VI $V_{9\flat}^{o}$ of IV   IV $V_{3\flat}^{o\,4}$ I

218

4. Harmonize the following melodies in open position, observing the following specifi-
cations:

1. augmented triad

2. diminished seventh

3. augmented sixth

4. Neapolitan sixth

*C-sharp in the bass.

5. STUDY AND ANALYSIS

The following complete compositions are suggested for study and analysis.

Schubert—*Schwanengesang:*
      XII. *Am Meer.*

Schumann—*Davidsbündlertänze, op. 6: No. 9.*

      Dichterliebe, op. 48:
        VI. *Im Rhein, im heiligen Strom;*
        XII. *Am leuchtenden Sommermorgen.*

Brahms—*Intermezzo, op. 76, No. 4;*

      Intermezzo, op. 76, No. 7;

      Capriccio, op. 116, No. 3;

      Intermezzo, op. 117, No. 2;

      Intermezzo, op. 119, No. 1.